Evie's Little Black Book

Hannah Pearl

Stories that inspire emotions
www.rubyfiction.com

Copyright © 2019 Hannah Pearl

Published 2019 by Ruby Fiction
Penrose House, Crawley Drive, Camberley, Surrey GU15 2AB, UK
www.rubyfiction.com

A CIP catalogue record for this book is available
from the British Library

ISBN: 978-1-91255-010-4

Printed and bound in Great Britain by Clays Ltd, Elcograf S.p.A.

To my husband.

*We all walk winding paths to get to where we end up,
and I'm very glad that I get to walk mine with you.*

Acknowledgements

This book wouldn't exist if it weren't for the team of people who picked me up and started to put me back together when my health fell apart.

I would like to thank my mum, dad, husband, children, brothers and sisters (both blood and in law).

To the team of parents who rallied round, got everyone to where they needed to be and became true and dear friends during this time, I owe you more than just a few words, but I hope that this goes some way to showing you all how much you mean to me. Thank you.

Thank you also to the Tasting Panel readers who passed the manuscript and made this all possible: Dimi E, Melissa C, Christina G, Jo O, Jenny K, Barbara B, Maureen W, Kathryn B, Katie P, Yvonne G and Bianca B.

Chapter One

The small ivory card had landed on my doorstep that Saturday morning. It looked so innocent, nestled amongst a handful of late birthday cards, but in fact it had been a bomb more potent even than the massive credit card bill and the summons for my annual dentist visit.

I crumpled up yet another tissue and threw it at the bin. It hit the tower of soggy hankies that were already in there and tumbled to the floor. I let out a plaintive wail and collapsed on the sofa. I cried until my eyes were red and puffy and my breath was coming in deep, hitching gasps.

Dragging myself to the cupboard, I opened a new slab of chocolate. Ten minutes later I was holding an empty wrapper and my stomach was feeling as delicate as my emotions. This called for desperate measures. I picked up my mobile and rang the first number on its speed dial.

'Hi, cuz,' Charmaine said. 'I was wondering when I'd hear from you.'

'Did you get one too?' I asked.

'This morning. I've called another chef in to cover my shift and I'm at the shop buying ice cream now. I'll be with you in ten minutes.' She hung up before I could tell her I was already feeling sick. Switching on my blues playlist on my iPod, I prepared to immerse myself entirely in my misery.

Charmaine let herself in with her key, walked up the stairs to my flat and looked at me with a mixture of concern and humour. Her hair was styled in braids, held loosely at the back with a black scrunchy band. Her lips were coloured red to coordinate with her tight top, which displayed an amount of cleavage I could never match. She leant over, unzipped her knee high boots, kicked them off and came and sat next to me on the sofa.

My flat was small, basically just the living room which was big enough for my two person sofa, an armchair – which had been there when I had moved in and which clashed with everything else, including modern fashion – a coffee table and TV. The three doors lined up along the back wall led to a tiny bathroom, functional kitchen, and a bedroom, which I called 'cosy' because calling it 'miniscule' might have been accurate, but felt depressing. It was all I'd been able to afford to rent after my hasty departure from my ex-fiancé's house, and life. It wasn't a lot to show for my twenty-six years on the planet, but it was my name on the lease, just mine, and I loved it.

Sitting down squashed together on my sofa, it was hard to tell that Charmaine towered over me by a good six inches. She put her arm around me, and I began crying again. She handed over the pot of my favourite cookies and cream ice cream and a spoon. My stomach churned at the thought of more sugar, but I dug in anyway.

'Are you going to go?' she asked.

'My parents will, they're coming back from their Spain trip especially, and Matt is George's best man, of course, being his best friend. It'll look really odd if I don't go. Plus, it's only a few miles up the road. They've rented that big hotel out in Stratford, you know, the one by the Olympic Stadium. I can't think of any plausible reason that will get me out of it. Are you going?'

'I wouldn't leave you there on your own,' she said, giving me a light squeeze. Charmaine was only born six months before me but it seemed that yet again my big cousin would be there to help me pick up the pieces of my life.

'You're the best.'

'I know,' she replied. 'Also, I want to be there to watch in case you try to stop the wedding when they ask if anyone has any objections.'

I shuddered at the thought. 'I still can't believe he's really getting married. This is the man who strung me along for years without ever even asking me out properly.'

'I still can't believe you were fooling around with your brother's best mate.'

'Ugh,' I groaned. 'That makes it sound so sordid. Besides, Matt went mad when he found out, as I'm sure you remember. It might have been okay for him and George to have a reputation, but heaven forbid his sister was one of the girls who got involved. I'm dreading his best man's speech.'

I handed Charmaine the half-eaten pot of ice cream and she dug in too.

'So what are you going to do?' she asked.

'Show up looking fabulous so that he can see what he missed, and cry in the toilets when it's over,' I told her.

'You might need to think about how you're going to accessorise your outfit to match your red eyes.' She handed me the small make-up mirror from her handbag. I looked and saw how swollen and blotchy my face was. This set me off weeping again. 'I was just kidding,' she said, handing me back the spoon. 'Let's turn this depressing music off for a start.' She reached over for my iPod and changed the playlist.

A moment later, Beyonce was singing to us about independent women, and I'd been sent off to splash my face with cold water and get dressed. 'Come on, Evie,' my cousin yelled. 'You need to get out and take your mind off him.'

'Shoe shopping?' I asked.

She nodded. 'Best therapy known to women. You've had your pity party, Evie O'Reilly, and now we're moving on.'

We took a bus into town and started at my favourite shoe shop in the world. It was tiny, with only two seats in the entire shop. Boxes were crammed floor to ceiling, and the scent of leather was strong and comforting.

'We haven't come to buy school shoes,' Charmaine said, wrinkling her nose at the sensible black sandals I was admiring. She closed the box, put it back on the stack and led me out. We walked a few doors further down the high street and went into a clothes shop that I never dared enter on my own. The music was loud and the shop assistants looked like models. I felt intimidated and held on to my cousin's arm.

She laughed, and led me towards the back where the shoes were. Picking up a pair of gladiator style sandals, she slipped her boots off and tried them on. Shaking her head, she slipped them off and tried on some silver sandals with strappy heels.

'If you buy those I'll need a stepladder to stand next to you,' I pointed out.

She laughed and handed me a pair of stilettos to try on.

'I might find something a little more subtle, and a little less neon pink,' I said, handing them back un-tested. 'They clash with my hair – and the red eyes I have from crying!'

'Then it's a good job I'm here to distract you,' she said, trying on a pair of green sparkly shoes which she, of course, looked gorgeous in.

We moved on to the shoe section of the giant department store that was at the front of the mall. Charmaine picked up some gold sequin ballet shoes, and I found a pair of strappy black shoes with a kitten heel. Happy with our purchases, we celebrated with some lunch in the brasserie on the top floor.

'So why are you so upset?' Charmaine asked as she tucked into her fries. They were golden and crispy, and I was already regretting not ordering some myself but my stomach still felt delicate after its breakfast of sugar and sorrowful reminiscences.

'It's not that I was expecting to marry him myself,' I said, helping myself to a chip from her plate. 'I guess I just didn't expect him to ever get married. And certainly not before I did. He never showed any inclination to settle down whilst I was seeing him.'

'Seeing him? Is that what you're calling it?' she said, with a loud snort.

'It sounds a bit less trampy than sleeping with repeatedly without ever actually going on a date,' I said, picking at my sandwich.

'Which I never really understood,' Charmaine continued. 'That wasn't your usual style.'

'I don't think I was successful enough with men to have a usual style.'

We finished our lunch. Well, Charmaine finished hers and I picked at a bit more of mine, and she stood up. 'What you need next,' she declared, 'is new underwear. I always feel better when I'm wearing really sexy knickers.'

She pulled the top of her pants up over her trousers to show me. I could see what looked like a piece of leopard print string, and I presumed her taste in underwear was a little skimpier than mine. An elderly gentleman on the next table choked on his tea. His wife slapped him on the back a little harder than she probably needed to and shot dirty looks at us. He was still looking red in the face and guilty by the time we had paid the bill.

Back out in the mall, I started heading to the shop where I usually bought my sensible cotton knickers, but again my cousin had other ideas. She dragged me into a brightly lit store filled with mannequins wearing what looked to me to be either see through netting or dental floss.

I searched and eventually found some women's boxer shorts, but Charmaine took them out of my basket and handed me something red and lacy. 'These will make you feel more confident,' she assured me. 'You don't need to dress like a schoolteacher all the time. It's been years since I saw you in anything sexy.'

I tried to get into the spirit of the trip and selected a few more pairs, though I wasn't convinced that I'd ever wear them. Handing over my credit card, I did feel a tiny thrill watching the sales assistant wrapping them in tissue paper and sealing them into a box. I had to admit it felt more luxurious than buying my usual multipack in a plastic bag.

Over a glass of wine back at my flat, I found myself getting maudlin again.

'Are you upset that you didn't get married first? Because if you ask me you had a lucky escape,' Charmaine asked. She had never liked Ryan. At first I'd put it down to their strong personalities competing with each other. Now I knew better. It wasn't simply a case of mutual distrust. He'd had a problem with anyone he couldn't boss around, and especially if they were female.

'You're right,' I said, topping up our glasses. 'Marrying Ryan would have been a huge mistake. I think he felt pressured into getting engaged because we'd been dating for a year and his mum kept asking about grandkids. He certainly let his grumpy side show more honestly once I had the ring on my finger.' That was putting it mildly, but I hadn't told Charmaine the worst of it. I was too embarrassed.

'Do you still miss him?' she asked.

I shook my head. 'Which tells me everything I need to know. Still, it would have been nice to have a plus one for George's wedding.' I started crying again. I took another huge swig of wine. Any more tears and I was at real risk of getting dehydrated. I'd never told Charmaine how unpleasant the last few months with Ryan had actually been. She was so strong and self-reliant, I hated to admit how downtrodden and crushed I'd become. She wouldn't understand how much I had come to see as 'normal', and what I'd put up with for the sake of a quieter time with him. Now that I was safely away from him I could scarcely believe some of it myself.

Charmaine stood up and guided me into my bedroom.

'Go and try some of your new underwear on and see if it cheers you up,' she suggested.

I sorted through the box, holding up a pair of tiny blue knickers covered in sparkly crystals. I had no idea what had come over me when I'd bought those. Luckily, at the bottom of the bag was a pair made of black lace. They were larger than the others, and I wouldn't be so worried about my unkempt bikini line in them. Slipping them on, I put the others away at the back of my drawer. It was then that the notebook caught my eye.

My little black book was actually a rather pretty floral notebook that I'd been given for my thirteenth birthday. And it wasn't filled with my conquests. Few as they were, that would have left an awful lot of blank pages. Instead it was filled with pages detailing every crush and every kiss I'd had since the first one I'd shared with Andy Brown in my friend's back garden when I was fifteen. At least half of the handwritten notes detailed the rise and fall of my crush on George Cooper, my brother's best friend, and the reason why I had spent the day in emotional turmoil.

I put my jeans back on, and walked back into the living room brandishing the notebook to show my cousin. 'In here,' I declared, 'are all my triumphs and mistakes.' Charmaine reached for the book but I pulled it away. I sat down and started flicking through the pages. 'Maybe if I look through this I can find out where I've been going wrong,' I told her.

'Is that your diary?' she asked.

'Almost,' I replied. 'This is a record of every guy I have ever fancied, kissed or more. If I read this, maybe I can work out why I'm still single and my commitment phobic ex is tying the knot.' I wondered if it would also help me remember a time when I'd felt attractive, let alone interested in men.

I drank more of my wine. 'Let's see,' I mused, turning back to the first page. 'Andy Brown, how did I mess that one up?'

Chapter Two

I woke up the next morning, sprawled on my sofa, empty pizza boxes on the floor, wine bottles on the table, and Charmaine asleep next to me. Her long legs dangled over the side. At some point she had changed into her new shoes, and the sequins glinted in the sunshine. I pulled my long ginger hair up into a bun and secured it out of the way.

Yawning, I stretched and got up to make coffee. If my cousin felt as rough as I did this morning we would need plenty of caffeine to get us moving again. I cleared the debris from the previous night and set out the cups and a plate of buttered toast.

'You're a star,' Charmaine mumbled, waking up and drinking from the mug I'd set next to her. 'And I think I've pinpointed the cause of your troubles.' She picked my floral notebook up from under her bottom and opened it. I reached for it before she could see just how pathetic I had been over the years, but she stood up and held it above her head so that I couldn't reach.

I glared at her, but sat down and listened to what she had to say.

'It's quite clear,' she continued, and I waited with baited breath for her answer to my problem, 'that you are single because your taste in men up until this point has been awful.'

I stuck my tongue out at her.

'Also, you might need to grow up a bit,' she said. 'Seriously, Evie. It isn't you. You're pretty.'

'I have wild hair and I'm short,' I pointed out.

'You have incredible, vibrant hair. And you're not short, you're petite,' she responded.

'I didn't mean for you to read that,' I said, pointing at the notebook.

'Sorry, cuz,' she said. 'You did give it to me last night. Around the time you brought out the tequila. Look, right here from page one where it starts with Andy, he was never good enough for you. What do you remember about the night you snogged him?'

I picked up a piece of toast and chewed as I thought back. 'I was excited that I'd been asked to go to a party. You helped me pick my outfit, do you remember?'

She nodded. 'We both went in jeans and denim jackets. Double denim. Double tragic.' She shuddered at the memory of some of our fashion disasters.

'Andy hardly spoke to me all night, you were busy with that guy you fancied.'

'Chris Ashling,' she supplied, sitting back and closing her eyes and smiling. No doubt remembering that she'd disappeared upstairs with him for half an hour and come back down with her top on inside out.

'I ended up stood in the kitchen drinking cider and listening to Penny complaining for hours about how her boyfriend wouldn't take her out for a McDonald's the night before. Eventually I went into the garden to get away from her, and when Andy came out for a smoke we got chatting.'

'And you had your first kiss it says here.' She pointed at a page. 'Doesn't sound like it was a very good one though.' She read:

'I had my first kiss last night! It was a bit weird, more sloppy than I was expecting. Is that normal?? It was with Andy Brown from school. I wonder if he really likes me. How do you tell? I'm going to see him in maths class later. I hope it isn't awkward. I wonder if I'll get to kiss him again. I'm glad we didn't bash heads or knock teeth at least!!'

I shook my head. 'I guess none of us had much experience back then. It was like kissing a slug. Who tasted like an ashtray. When we pulled back I had to wipe my mouth dry.'

Charmaine groaned, and I decided to spare her from any further details given her delicate state.

'I saw him the other day,' she said. 'I drove past the garage where he works.' She paused for a moment. 'Didn't you say you needed a new tyre for your Mini?'

I nodded, then realised a moment later what she was suggesting. 'I'm not going to get it there though. Can you imagine how embarrassing that would be? He'd think I was stalking him.'

'Or, he'd see you looking fabulous and realise what he missed out on, and you might accept that you're a babe, and it isn't your fault that you haven't met the love of your life yet.'

'It might not be open. It's a Sunday.'

'Luckily for you, his is the only garage around here that is open. I guess breakdowns happen every day of the week so today they've got no competition.'

'Lucky me,' I muttered. Charmaine just grinned at me. 'Looking fabulous?'

She nodded. 'I'll help you,' she said.

An hour later my hair was washed and hung in a long braid down my back. I was wearing skinny jeans. I'd refused to go into a garage wearing a miniskirt as Charmaine had suggested, but I had agreed that as it was June and quite warm, I'd skip the jacket that I'd wanted to cover up with, and wear a vest top. Tugging up the neck of it and wishing I had chosen something that at least covered my bra fully, I got out of the car.

Immediately two of the mechanics stopped what

they were doing and walked over to help. I could hear Charmaine giggling in the passenger seat.

'My right front tyre keeps going flat,' I said. 'I think I have a slow puncture.'

'You've come to the right place,' the younger man said, wiping his hands on an oily rag and tossing it onto the counter. He ran his hand through his hair, leaving a greasy mark on his forehead. It was almost impossible to talk to him without staring at it.

'Do you think I need a new one?' I asked.

'We might be able to patch it up for a while which is the cheaper option,' said his mate, doing the buttons up on his overalls to cover his belly, 'but a new tyre would be safest.'

They began to talk me through the various tyres that they had in stock, and I tried really hard to concentrate on what they were saying, though to me the three choices seemed pretty much identical. 'I think I'll just get a new one,' I told them, mostly so they would stop talking about all the different options.

'Is Andy in today?' Charmaine asked, getting out of the car. The last mechanic who had been tinkering under the bonnet on a Ford turned at the sight of my cousin and walked over to talk to us too.

'He's just nipped out for a spare part. Should be back any minute. Do you know him?'

'We used to go to school with him,' I said. 'Thought we might as well say hi whilst we're here.'

The older guy pointed to their office and told us to help ourselves to a cup of tea. 'You can wait in there if you like. Andy should be back by the time we've fitted your new tyre.'

Charmaine and I wandered past the remains of several exhaust pipes and an engine. We looked at the mugs that were stood next to the kettle, but the line of grime around the bottoms put us off using them. If they had been washed this century then they could only have been dried with another of the greasy rags to leave them in this state.

'Remind me again what we're doing here?' I asked her.

'We're proving that it isn't you, it's them, the guys you've been choosing,' she said, gesturing at the younger mechanic who had his hand between his legs and was currently giving his own personal junk a thorough inspection.

'Maybe he just has an itch?' I said.

'Does that make you any more likely to want to go near him?' she asked.

I shook my head and hoped that if he couldn't get his hands out of his trousers soon that he would go to see a doctor.

The car was ready and I was just paying when Andy strolled in. He set a small paper bag on the counter, and his colleague called him over to greet us. 'Got your mates in, Andy,' he called out.

Andy walked over, and the first thing I noticed was that although his face remained remarkably unchanged over the last ten years, his hair was already considerably thinner. He wiped his hands on his overall and held one out for me to shake. He licked his lips and I could see the tongue I remembered so well sneaking out. I felt a shiver go down my spine, and not in a pleasant way.

'Nice to see you again, Evie,' he said. 'Good choice of car. A right little goer.' He winked and my stomach heaved, even though my hangover had long since passed.

'We just stopped in for a tyre,' I said. 'Thought we'd say hi whilst we were here.'

'I'm almost finished if you fancy going for a drink,' he said. I could see his tongue poking out of the side of his mouth. It still looked slimy.

I shook my head. 'Sorry, we've got to run, but it was nice bumping into you again.'

I got back in the car and started the engine. Driving us home, I watched Charmaine rocking with laughter.

'What was so funny?' I asked.

'You,' she said. 'You couldn't get away quick enough.'

'Did you see how he licked his lips when he saw me?' I asked. 'I can't believe I ever went there.' I shuddered. 'I could almost see him drool and I've had enough of his spit on me to last a lifetime already.' Even the memory of his kiss made me feel grubby and I wiped my mouth.

We got out of the car and went back up to my flat. Charmaine picked up the notebook and flicked through a few pages. 'It proves my point though,' she said. 'You certainly wouldn't have chosen to marry Andy, so there wasn't anything wrong with you that time. Now, who was next in here?'

'Bill Banks,' I said, sitting back on the sofa. 'And he was dreamy.'

'What happened?'

'Don't you remember?' I asked. She shook her head. 'He kissed me at the school leavers' party, then when I saw him at college after the summer holidays he blanked me. I cried on your shoulder for a week about that.'

She began to read from my little black book – or rather from my floral notebook. *'The party was great, much better than I thought it would be, mostly because I got to make out with Bill! He's so cute. He's really tall and strong. I didn't even know he knew who I was. He's always busy playing football and yelling at the first years who dare to go near the pitch.'*

I cringed at the memory. I'd been so chuffed that he paid me some attention and so crushed afterwards when I realised that I had read more into it than he had meant.

'There's an address for him in here,' she said, showing me the page.

'I always used to do that, I don't know why. There's probably either an address or a phone number, sometimes even a photo, for most of the guys in there.' The plan to look up my exes had never occurred to me before, and I wondered why I had gone to such lengths to note so many personal details down about them. Perhaps it was just to prove to myself that they were real. I'd been something of a late bloomer where boys were concerned.

'This is only round the corner,' Charmaine said, standing up again.

'Oh no,' I said, shaking my head. 'I've had enough humiliation for one day.'

'Don't you want to check, make sure Andy wasn't a one-off?'

'Do you really think chasing a guy who kissed me once at a party a decade ago will help me feel better?' I asked.

'There's only one way to find out.'

Chapter Three

I can't believe I'm doing this, I thought, as I found myself alone, knocking on the door. I had no idea how I was going to explain to whoever opened it what I was doing. If Bill himself opened the door I wasn't sure whether I would wet myself or run away. Charmaine had been insistent though and I'd folded in the face of her confidence. So I here I was, waiting on the doorstep of a guy I'd fancied for a few weeks when I was sixteen.

I was preparing to apologise when the door opened, and I completely forgot what I'd planned to say. The man standing before me was dressed in jeans and a soft cotton shirt. He had light brown hair, a beard, and bare feet. 'Yes,' he said, looking at me. I stared back. He was beautiful. Not handsome exactly, his jawline was hidden by the hair, and his fringe was a little long and kept getting in his eyes. He swept it back out of the way again and looked at me.

'I live round the corner,' I began. 'I was just looking for an old school friend who used to live here when ...' He was the most attractive man I'd seen in a long time, and I found myself getting tongue-tied. Kicking myself for being so awkward, I was about to try again. 'I'm—'

My explanation was interrupted when a small blonde child appeared and gripped his leg. Behind him, a beeping noise began, joined a moment later by what sounded like a smoke alarm.

'Blast,' he said, looking around in confusion as he tried to work out what to do, look after the kid or stop the house from burning down.

I noticed hair bands amongst the curls and realised that

she was a little girl, probably about three years old, and what's more, I recognised her. I'd volunteered to run some story sessions in the library over the Christmas holidays, trying to distract myself from the feelings of loneliness after Ryan had dumped me. She had been there with a young woman who had been more interested in her phone than the sparky kid she was supposed to be looking after. 'It's Alice, isn't it? Do you remember me from story time? We read *Santa's Little Helper*.' Actually, we'd read it twice as the children had loved it so much. The adults had all looked relieved that for once it wasn't them reading the same book on repeat.

'Let me help,' I told the man, offering my hand to Alice. I wouldn't have been so forward with a child under normal conditions, but the alarm was still sounding and the smoke that now reached the front door was black and acrid. 'I'm a teacher,' I said to reassure him that it was safe to leave Alice with me whilst he saved the house. She took my hand and he seemed to relax. Alice and I waited on the front step, singing nursery rhymes and chatting until the alarm stopped. The silence seemed deafening in its wake.

'It's safe to come in,' the man said, returning to the doorstep to fetch us. I followed him into the house, thankful for the reprieve and at the same time wondering what I'd walked into.

He had opened the oven door and dropped the smoking tray into the sink. The air was thick with grey fog, and I threw open the back door so that we could breathe.

'Uncle Jake burnt the cake,' Alice said. Then, hearing the pleasing rhyme she had come up with, she started dancing around the kitchen chanting, 'Uncle Jake burnt the cake' over and over again, getting louder with each repetition, until the man who I now surmised was the Uncle Jake with questionable baking skills, picked her up and tickled her.

'Okay, squirt, would you like a programme whilst I clean up in here?' he asked.

The little girl squealed and ran off. He followed her and I was left alone in the kitchen, looking around at the trail of destruction. There was flour all over the floor, broken eggshells on the long wooden counter that ran across the sidewall under the windows, and the sink held only charred remains of their efforts.

I picked up the remains of the eggs and threw them in the bin. There was a kitchen roll holder bolted to the wall, so I grabbed a handful and started wiping up the worst of the flour. I'd just run in a sink full of hot soapy water when I realised I had company.

'Sorry,' Jake said. 'You caught us in the middle of attempting to make my sister a birthday cake.'

'I'm sorry, I didn't mean to ruin your efforts.'

'I suspect it was destined for the bin long before you arrived,' he said with a sigh.

'Was this your first try at baking?' I asked.

He nodded. 'It's my sister's first birthday on her own since her divorce so I thought I'd come and stay with her and Alice for a while. She's at work. She's an office manager and they had a break-in overnight, so she's been up to her neck in paperwork and cleaning up on what should have been her day off. We wanted to greet her with her favourite lemon drizzle cake. It said online that the recipe was a good one to make with kids. I don't know where we went wrong.'

I looked at my watch. 'It's only two o'clock,' I pointed out. 'Do you have more ingredients? I'll stay and help, if you like.'

I was surprised at myself as I offered but when he looked up and I could see the relief on his face I was pleased that I'd suggested I help.

'Would you mind?' he asked. He held out his hand. 'I haven't even introduced myself. I'm Jake Archer.'

'Evie O'Reilly,' I said, shaking his hand. I rolled up my sleeves and we started measuring. I handed him the bowl and asked him to cream the sugar and butter whilst I weighed the flour. I leant past him to sift it into his bowl, and felt my pulse pick up as I accidentally brushed against his arm.

'I meant to say, was there something I can help you with?' Jake asked. 'I was so distracted by the flames I forgot to ask.'

'Flames? You mean the cake was actually on fire?' I replied.

Jake nodded.

'Impressive,' I told him.

He gave a small bow.

'Thanks, but I was just looking up someone I used to go to school with.' This was true, but it was only half of the picture. Jake, standing with flour in his hair and soot on his shirt, was pretty cute and suddenly I wasn't sure that I wanted to tell him any more details about why I was on my mission. I handed him a sieve and tried to distract him from asking any more questions. 'Make sure there are no lumps in the flour,' I told him.

We had to improvise and use a loaf tin to bake the cake, as the one Jake had used for his first attempt was black and charred. 'You might owe your sister a new baking tin,' I said.

'It was just the three of us; me, Bea and my dad for most of my life. I owe her a lot more than that. That's another reason I wanted to do something nice for her. She's not much of a cook either, though she's been trying recently. I thought it would be nice for her to come home to the smell of fresh baking. Thank goodness you stopped by,' Jake said, putting the new cake in the oven and setting a timer. 'This might have been where we went wrong last time. I forgot to check how long it had been in the oven, and then Alice needed the loo. And, well, you saw what happened.'

I grinned. 'You should have seen my first baking experiments,' I told him. 'I got hooked on marble cakes for a while.'

'That sounds pretty hard on your teeth,' Jake said.

'It refers to the colouring,' I told him. He smiled at me as he scrubbed the tin, and I found myself smiling back. 'You're supposed to put gentle waves of coloured batter through the mix to give a marbling effect. I didn't go for the subtle approach though. I wonder now how my parents used to eat these hideously green or blue cakes and not complain.'

Alice wandered back into the kitchen looking sleepy. She had a tatty old blanket in one hand and her thumb in her mouth. 'Wanna drink, Uncle Jake,' she said.

'Say please,' he told her.

'Say please,' she echoed. He got up and poured some milk into a sippy cup.

He picked her up and then sat with her on his knee. She snuggled against him as she drank. I wondered how it felt to be in his arms. I tried to snap my attention back to the reason I was there. 'I mentioned earlier, I was looking for someone I went to school with who used to live here but it seems that they must have moved. I don't suppose you know where they went, do you?'

'I can ask my sister when she gets home,' Jake said. 'She only bought the house about six months ago and might have a forwarding address.'

'That would be great,' I said, standing up. Alice yawned again and I thought I'd better head off and leave him to look after her.

'Why don't you come back at seven tonight? You deserve a slice of the cake given that you baked it, and you can ask Bea about the previous owners.'

I flushed at his offer, but as I watched, he was so engrossed in looking after his niece that his invitation seemed to be really just a simple offer of food and a chat. I accepted.

We paused in the hall and he leaned in close to me. I pulled back, bumping into the coats, which hung from hooks opposite the door.

'Just opening the door,' he explained.

If Jake wondered why I'd nearly jumped out of my skin when he got close, he was too polite to ask. I wasn't sure I could explain it myself. I made myself hold out my hand to shake his. He looked a little quizzical at that, but he was a gentleman and didn't leave me hanging. He held my hand for a fraction of a second longer than I expected and I felt my cheeks begin to flush again. It was a drawback of having such bright hair and pale skin. When I blushed there was nothing subtle about it. I went scarlet.

Ducking past him, I gave a wave and headed off as quickly as I could. Back home, I began berating myself for not being calmer when Jake was near me. I wanted to change my top as it was covered in flour and smelt of smoke, but as I lifted it I caught a waft of Jake's aftershave. I breathed it in, then realised what I was doing. I balled the T-shirt and threw it straight in the wash. Then I showered and washed my hair for good measure.

Standing in front of my wardrobe, I picked out my favourite black jeans. I planned to dress down, though it wasn't as if I often went out any other way in truth. I was only going back that evening to try and find Bill's address. Then again, I was crashing a birthday tea, so maybe I should dress a little smarter. In the end I compromised with a burnt orange silk blouse that complemented my hair. I tried to put the beautiful man out of my mind as I buttoned it up and dug out my long neglected bottle of perfume.

I tried to mark a few essays whilst I was waiting but the set assignment for this year was drier than I remembered, and I found myself struggling for motivation. It was definitely the essays, and not the distraction of Jake. I told myself that a few times and tried to get myself to believe it. I set myself the goal of getting through six before I went out. The more I could get through today, the easier tomorrow would be. Besides, it was only a few weeks until the summer holidays. How much more marking could I get stuck with before then?

Chapter Four

I knocked on Jake's door bang on seven, carrying a bottle of wine for Bea's birthday that I hoped would pair well with the replacement cake, and was greeted with a much calmer welcome this time. A tired-looking woman, perhaps only an inch or two taller than my five foot three, opened the door. She had the same blonde curly hair I'd seen on the little girl earlier and I presumed that she was Alice's mum.

'I'm Evie,' I said. 'Jake asked me to come back at seven tonight.'

She showed me back into the kitchen, and I was relieved to find that it no longer smelt of smoke. 'Hi,' said Jake, getting up and kissing my cheek. I flushed, and bent down to say hello to Alice in the hopes it would fade before the adults noticed.

'Uncle Jake burnt the cake,' she told me solemnly.

'He did, sweetie,' I agreed. 'But then he made a new one. Was it tasty?'

'It was,' Bea said. 'And I believe we have you to thank.'

'It was no problem,' I assured her.

Alice started to yawn and rub her eyes.

'I think it's someone's bedtime,' Bea said, reaching down and scooping up her little girl. She carried Alice over for a goodnight kiss from her uncle, and Alice reached out to me so I gave her a goodnight kiss too, and Bea carried her up to bed.

'Bea will be down in half an hour,' Jake assured me. 'Why don't we have a glass of wine and a slice of your delicious cake whilst we wait? I'm sure that Bea will want a drink when she comes down. She's had a long day but she thinks that the worst of the clean up in her office is done now.

'So you live locally?' Jake asked as we sat down with our drinks. 'You mentioned something earlier about knowing Alice from the library?'

'I have a flat just round the corner,' I said. 'I'm an English teacher at the local secondary school. I was only helping out in the library for a few sessions during the holidays. It was good for me to keep busy.' I regretted the last sentence as soon as I'd said it, and hoped that Jake didn't ask what I was trying to distract myself from. I hurried to change the subject. 'What do you do when you're not here being super-uncle?'

He laughed. 'I'm not sure how super I was today. I'm here helping out while I job hunt. Trying to be useful, mostly succeeding, today aside.'

'Alice looked pretty happy,' I pointed out.

'She's a remarkably calm kid. Which is lucky really, I don't know how Bea would have managed otherwise.'

'This must have been pretty tough on her.'

He nodded. 'They were childhood sweethearts and I don't think she saw the split coming. I think he just couldn't handle being a full-time dad, so he left. But to answer your question, I've just finished my master's degree and I'm taking a little time out to think about what comes next. My first degree was from art college, and I spent a couple of years travelling around the country painting and helping in workshops and at galleries, but it's a tough field to make a living in. I think I'm going to try and make an income as a graphic designer, keep the art as a hobby for a while. I've spent a few weeks sending out CVs and registering with employment agencies but it seems to be a tricky market at the moment and I fear it's going to take longer than I expected. It seemed to make sense to do that here and try and be useful while I apply. The nanny Bea had hired decided to move to Spain to follow her boyfriend at short notice, so I said I'd help out until she got something else sorted. On the off chance that I do score a job at least it'll give her a few weeks to find something else, as most companies are used to people working out notice so they'd not expect me to start the next day. Plus, it's lovely to have some extra time with Alice.'

'I'm glad you're here,' I said, before realising what I'd said and trying to backtrack. 'I mean, I'm glad for your sister that she has you here.' I picked up my glass and took a long drink. I thought I heard Jake chuckle, but when I looked at him he was composed. He picked up the bottle and filled my glass again.

Jake was clearly a doting uncle, and was busy recounting how much fun he and Alice had been having when Bea came back in. Her eyes were red, and I wondered whether she was tired or whether she had been crying.

Jake got up and fetched a clean glass for her. 'Happy birthday,' I said, raising my glass to touch hers.

'Thank you, and thanks for your help earlier. I gather you helped clean the kitchen too.'

'I'm sure Jake had it all in hand,' I said, and she raised a perfectly manicured eyebrow at him. 'Well, almost under control,' I said. They both smiled, but Jake's easy laugh seemed to have left him temporarily.

'Evie came looking for the couple who used to live here before you bought the place,' Jake told her.

Bea got up and started hunting through the junk drawer next to the sink. 'I had their forwarding address somewhere. Lovely elderly couple they were, they left us a bottle of champagne as a moving in present.'

'Elderly?' I repeated, trying to work out how old Bill's

25

parents would have been. 'Oh dear, maybe they weren't the people I was looking for after all.'

'Who were you trying to find?' asked Jake.

I blushed again, and wondered how to explain what I was up to. 'I used to go to school with the children who lived here. I'm looking up a few old faces and wondered if I could get in touch with them.' If Jake and Bea wondered why finding old friends might make my face turn the colour of beetroot they were too polite to ask. I didn't like to think about how defeated I felt. I'd only managed to look up one guy from my book so far and didn't want to give up yet. But perhaps this task wasn't meant to be.

'The Smiths next door might know,' Bea said, thinking it over. 'As far as I can tell they've lived here forever. I'll pop round in the morning and ask them. Let's swap mobile numbers just in case I find anything.'

'Thank you,' I said, breathing a quiet sigh of relief. Maybe I'd find answers yet as to why my love life was so unsuccessful.

'Why don't you come back for dinner tomorrow evening? It would be nice to thank you properly for your help today. We can let you know what they say. Alice would enjoy it, she seems very fond of you,' Jake said.

'She just remembers me from story time and knows that I'll read stories again and again if asked,' I told them.

'Speaking of which, I said I'd go back up again in a few minutes to give her another kiss and a story. So tomorrow then, and don't worry, I'll be doing the cooking,' Bea said, and I grinned.

It was so hard to concentrate the next day at school. Mondays felt long even at the best of times, but this one seemed to last forever, and my mind kept drifting to my plans for the evening. Eventually though I finished work and dragged myself out for a jog round the park. If I didn't burn off some of this nervous energy I would hardly be able to sit still for the meal.

I showered and dug out a light summer dress from the back of my wardrobe. Usually I was a jeans and baggy shirt kind of a girl, but suddenly I felt like trying to make an attempt at looking more feminine.

Knocking on the door for the third time in two days, I wondered why I was going to so much effort to track down a boy I'd kissed once a decade earlier. At least, I told myself that was the reason I was here. I tried not to think about why I'd taken an extra minute to swipe on some mascara and lip gloss before walking over. Then I remembered George's wedding, and my failed love affairs, and resolved to continue on my mission.

Bea answered the door and I handed her a bunch of flowers.

'Thank you,' she said as I followed her down the hall and back into her kitchen. It felt warm and cosy inside, and smelt of roast chicken. I could hear Jake and Alice playing football and giggling in the back garden.

I swallowed and realised my mistake but wasn't sure how to rectify it. As she started to place dishes on the side I plucked up my courage and blurted it out. 'I think I forgot to say yesterday that I'm a vegetarian.'

Bea set the knife down with a clunk next to the chicken and stared at me for a moment without speaking. 'No problem,' she said eventually, as though struck by inspiration. She crossed to the fridge and got out a box of eggs. 'I'll whip up a quick omelette.' Bea called Jake and Alice in and told them to wash their hands.

'I'm sorry,' I said, getting up to help. I'd been vegetarian since I was thirteen and had got used to letting people know. I must have been more flustered than I had realised the day before to have forgotten. Thank goodness Bea

27

seemed to take the change of plans in her stride. She guided me back to my seat.

'Alice will share some with you anyway, I'm sure.'

I apologised again. 'I usually tell people beforehand, I was just distracted yesterday.' I saw a slight smile cross Jake's face and I wondered what he thought had made it slip my mind. 'I was busy thinking about my mission,' I continued.

'Your mission?' Jake said, his green eyes twinkling in the spotlights set into the kitchen ceiling.

Bea lit the hob and poured a jug of beaten eggs into a pan. A few moments later she flipped a perfectly cooked omelette onto a plate and set it on the table.

'Thank you,' I said, and she smiled.

'Don't worry, I usually end up cooking a second tea for Alice anyway when she changes her mind about what she'll eat.'

On hearing her name Alice put down her teddy and began to bang her spoon on the table. Jake took it from her and she looked like she was about to cry so he gave it back. She banged it again. 'I hungry,' she announced. Bea offered her a piece of chicken, but she continued to play with the spoon. Bea removed the chicken and gave her some omelette. Alice tucked in straight away.

I tucked in, helping myself to the roast potatoes and wilted spinach on the side. 'This is delicious,' I said, and Bea looked pleased.

'I had a quick chat with Mrs Smith next door,' Jake said, reminding me of why I was there. 'She remembered the Banks family who used to live here, I assume that's who you were after, but I'm afraid she didn't have a forwarding address for them.'

My face must have showed how deflated I felt, but Jake smiled as he produced his final piece of news. 'She did, however, know where their youngest son works. Apparently Bill has a shop on the high street.'

'That's great news. I'll pop in and see him there,' I said.

'You might need to think about that,' Jake said, and I stared at him.

'He runs the butcher shop.'

Chapter Five

My fifth year students were on study leave leading up to their exams, and so on Tuesday I had a longer lunch break than usual. I rarely left the school during the day, but I couldn't bring myself to wait until Saturday to go to Bill's shop. Charmaine had been convinced that I would find the answers I needed, and though once I had sobered up I had been less certain, I decided to trust her and do my best to continue the search.

I thought back to what I'd written about Bill in my little black book. *'Saw Bill at college today. I was heading up the hill to my first English Lit class. He was heading down to where the training kitchens were. I wasn't sure whether to say anything, he hasn't texted me since we snogged at the party. Charmaine says I can text him if I want, but I'm pretty sure that if he wanted to talk to me he'd have got in touch. He had so many mates around him, maybe he didn't see me when I waved. I hope they were just laughing at something someone said and not at me. Why did I wave? It was so dorky. I just want to find someone who really likes ME!!'*

Outside in the warm sun the smell of raw meat coming from inside the shop was overpowering. I tried to gather my confidence before I walked in. I set one foot onto the sawdust-covered floor and instantly recognised the man stood at the back behind the counter. Bill was wielding a sharp knife and cutting a huge hunk of ribs set on a wooden block. A row of chickens hung from hooks behind him, and a pig's head stared at me from inside the fridge cabinet.

I was already having second thoughts; the setting was

all too macabre for a vegetarian, even without the red-faced six foot hulk of an ex wielding a blade. Still, I'd made it this far so I breathed through my mouth in the hope of being able to escape the smell, and tried to work out how to introduce myself. Just then a young lad in a white coat walked behind Bill. He picked up a long tube of salami from the cooked meat fridge and turned to lay it on the slicer. He accidentally bumped Bill, who spat swear words at him as he ducked quietly away.

'Can I help you,' Bill called out as he finally spotted me at the door.

'I've changed my mind,' I said, thinking for a second time that week that I'd had a lucky escape. It seemed that he hadn't changed his self-centred ways since I'd last seen him.

I met Charmaine in the pub that night to update her on my progress and to discuss stage three of my plan. I moaned about how it had taken me so many days to locate Bill, only to find out that he too was best left in the past.

'Jake sounds like a nice bloke,' she said as she sipped her pint. I'd tried to skim over my reaction to him but obviously hadn't done a very good job.

'He is, and he's great with Alice,' I replied.

'Did you get his number then?'

'I've sworn off men until I work out where I've been going wrong,' I reminded her. 'I don't want to get hurt again.'

She reached across and squeezed my hand. 'So who is next?'

I hadn't brought my little black book out with me. The danger of losing it and having a complete stranger read my tales of teenage angst was more than I could bear. I didn't need to check though, I could remember all too clearly.

'It was the Christmas party at college. I was sixteen, and smitten. He was in a band and I thought he was the greatest thing since sliced bread.' I'd written about how it had felt to flirt with him. *'He's so cute. And he keeps smiling when he catches my eye.'*

Charmaine sat forward watching me. 'Long-haired Nick?' she asked.

I nodded.

'There was about ten pages in my notebook talking about how much I fancied him, and then another twenty trying to work out why he dumped me and trying to work out what I'd done wrong.'

'Did you ever stop to think that it might not have been you?' my cousin pointed out. 'Teenage boys are hardly the best models of rational thought.'

I shrugged at her. I knew she was right, but if there was a chance that I could find out for sure, I was going to take it.

'How are you going to find him?' she asked.

'I don't know. I didn't have an address for him in my book. He hadn't gone out with me for long enough for me to find it out. There was a photo of him performing at college, and I had noted down which classes he was in, but that won't help me find him now.'

'Have you googled him?' Charmaine asked. I was astounded that the simple idea had eluded me all day.

'I didn't think of that,' I admitted. I pulled out my mobile and brought up a search engine screen. 'There are pages of Nick Fosters,' I said dejectedly, scrolling down. And down, and down.

'Add the word guitar, and then try under the images,' she suggested.

I tapped a few buttons on the screen and there was Nick, staring back at me. 'He's still got the long hair,' I said, turning my phone so that Charmaine could see. 'It looks like he's still in a band.' I clicked a few of the links and found myself on their home page.

Charmaine reached for the phone. 'It says here that they've got some gigs coming up.'

I looked where she was pointing, and clicked again. 'These are all over the country. Is that a good thing?' I asked. 'Does that mean that they're sought after, or that they're so desperate for gigs that they'll play anywhere?'

'This one is pretty local,' she said, pointing at one of the lines of vivid blue text on the otherwise black background. 'It's only about half an hour away. We could go and see them.'

Sneaking in to a gig where it would be dark and Nick would be busy concentrating on his music meant that he would be far less likely to see me, unless I wanted him to. 'That's a great idea. It would be nice to find out that one of my former crushes isn't either greasy or just plain nasty now.'

'You could become his groupie,' she said, laughing at me.

Ten years earlier and I probably would have. Now though I was older, if not wiser. There was a box with contact details for the band in case you wanted to order their CD, and over the next few days I toyed with the idea of emailing Nick before the performance but I wasn't sure how to explain why I was getting in touch. I didn't want him to think that I'd been desperately missing him for years.

The pub where Nick's band was playing was just around the corner from where my brother Matt lived, so Charmaine and I decided to invite ourselves over for dinner. It gave us the chance to pretend that should Nick turn out to be relatively normal and we got chatting, we could legitimately use the excuse that we had happened to be in the area.

Matt was pleased to see us and greeted us both with a hug at the door. He showed us into his house, and I was immediately glad that we had brought a takeaway with us. Living with three other single men, the air inside was fragranced with hints of dirty football gear, and washing up that was still awaiting attention. It was usually safer to bring food that could be eaten straight from the container.

I passed round boxes of pizza whilst Charmaine handed out cans of pop. She had wisely suggested that we didn't risk using the glasses either. I shifted a stack of *Viz* magazines and sat on the manky brown sofa, where I immediately sank so low that I'd need a hand when it was time to get up. My cousin watched me and decided to take a chance on sitting on the floor instead. I wished I had done the same, until she let out a shriek and shot up.

'Something tickled me,' she cried. 'That better not have been a rodent or I'm never coming to visit this skanky hole again.'

I pulled my feet up off the floor and tucked them underneath me on the sofa just in case.

Matt laughed and reached behind her. 'It was just an old sock, you must have sat up against it,' he said, holding up a piece of fabric. It was thick with mud, and had been under the sofa for long enough that big balls of fluff were stuck to it.

'That's no better than a rat,' Charmaine squealed.

Matt picked it up and waved it at her and we both screamed at him. He laughed, finding himself hilarious, until a ball of dust detached from the sock and floated gently down until it landed on his pizza.

'Jonno,' he shouted up the stairs, 'it's your turn to clean this bloody place. It's turning into a dump.' 'Turning into' gave it more credit than the house deserved. It had passed dump status about three black bin bags and a decent vacuuming ago.

Matt blew the dust off the pizza, but thankfully he didn't eat that slice. Instead he took it out and rested it on top of the empty box on the coffee table.

'So what are your plans for this evening?' he asked us. 'Not that I'm complaining about having my dinner provided.'

'We're off to the Standard,' I said. 'There's a band playing that we thought we'd check out.'

Just then Matt's flatmate, Big Steve, walked in, swiped the dirty piece of pizza and ate it as he went upstairs. Charmaine and I looked at each other and shuddered. Matt didn't even notice and carried on talking. 'That sounds all right,' he said, taking a swig from his can of Coke. 'Let's clear up here and I'll come with you.'

'What's to clean? We didn't use any of your stuff?' Charmaine pointed out as Matt shooed her into the kitchen.

'You wash and I'll dry,' he said, pointing at the mountain of dirty pots in the sink.

'None of that is ours,' I pointed out.

'If we don't get it done soon I won't have time to come out,' he said.

'I don't want you to,' I argued, wondering what he would say if he realised who we were going to watch.

'Come on, you don't really want me to have mice in the house, do you?' he asked.

I sighed, long used to the games my brother played to score some extra help, and started scrubbing. Charmaine grabbed a black bin bag and started throwing out all the empty food boxes, which littered the surfaces. She also chucked a pan which contained food remnants so carbonised it was impossible to tell what the cook had been attempting to make in the first place. Matt disappeared off claiming he was going to look for a clean tea towel so that he could dry up, but I figured that was probably a futile gesture. This household didn't seem that concerned with housework or hygiene.

When he came back downstairs he had changed clothes and gelled his hair. The kitchen was looking slightly less like a bomb site. He didn't have a tea towel with him. 'Couldn't find a clean one after all, so these might as well drip dry whilst we're out,' he said, gesturing at the now sparkling set of plates.

'Let's go,' Charmaine said, tugging on her jacket. 'I need a wee and there's no way I'm going to use the loo here without a gas mask.' We headed out to make the short walk to the pub.

The Standard was huge, built around three hundred years ago, when the area was still mostly woods. Today, Epping Forest remained as a reminder of the rural past, but increasing numbers of houses had grown around its outskirts, hence the crowds milling around outside waiting to go in and hear Nick's band. Rumour had it that the front bar area was haunted by a ghost of an old highwayman who was caught and hung on the site shortly before the pub was built. I wasn't sure I believed the tales, but I tried to avoid having to order the drinks, just in case.

The previous landlord had extended the bar area at the back and added a stage. I'd been to a couple of gigs here when I was a teenager, but hadn't been since I'd returned from university. It hadn't changed a bit; the old wooden benches at the back were still too narrow and too hard to be comfortable. I handed Matt some cash and asked him to fetch the drinks. He laughed at my being a scaredy-cat, but went anyway. Sometimes it was nice to have a big brother.

The warm up band were playing and there was a decent crowd already, though I expected it to get busier as the evening wore on. The room felt cosy, with its low ceilings, and a pit at the back where open fires were lit in winter. The warmth of a June evening, coupled with the body heat from the people dancing, meant that there would be no need for one tonight.

Matt returned carrying a round of beers and handed us each a bottle. More people crowded in, and we found ourselves being edged nearer the stage. The band played their final song and we cheered as they packed up. I took my jacket off and dropped it onto a bench.

My heart began to race as the band packed away their instruments and the stagehands began to set up for Nick's band. I was just about to chicken out and nip to the loo when Nick himself came onto the stage and plugged in his guitar. He looked striking, lit up by a spotlight against the black stage, complete with black curtains.

He played a few chords and asked the tech guy at the back to adjust the settings. He sang a line into the microphone, unleashing an ear-splitting feedback loop that caused me to cover my ears. Charmaine grinned and gave me a thumbs up and I was glad that someone was finding this funny.

Matt nudged me and shouted in my ear, 'Hey, isn't that the bloke you used to fancy at college?'

Sadly, he shouted this just as the wail ended and the room had fallen quiet. A ripple of laughter went round the crowd, and Nick paused from his preparation to look at who was talking. He walked over to the edge of the stage. I tried to step back but by now there were so many people in the room I couldn't escape.

'Evie?' he asked, as he noticed who I was.

Chapter Six

The band were actually really good and, if I hadn't been feeling so embarrassed all evening, I would probably have enjoyed the music. Nick looked great, he stripped down to a tight black vest for the final songs, and his arms displayed some impressive biceps that hadn't been there when I knew him. He must have been putting in some serious gym time these days.

He'd asked me to stay and join him for a drink after they finished playing. I wanted to skip out, but Charmaine pointed out that there was no point in me retracing my past if I kept running away from it. I sucked it up and waited, my heart pounding, to see if I could learn anything about where I'd gone wrong with Nick.

I'd initially met him through a mutual friend. The lead singer of his old band had been in my English Literature A-level class and a group of us had gone along to hear them play one night. Nick had been spellbinding to watch as he rocked out to their music, hair flying as he danced. I'd been captivated, and when the band had joined us for a drink afterwards, I couldn't keep my eyes off him. He'd noticed, and had offered to walk me home. When he kissed me on the doorstep I'd found myself pressing against him. He was the first guy I'd kissed who really moved me.

Sadly, I don't think I'd moved him as much, as we had a couple of dates and I was just starting to think of him as an actual (whisper the word), boyfriend, when he unceremoniously dumped me. I'd never known why, but perhaps by the end of tonight I might pluck up the courage to ask him.

Charmaine and Matt danced crazily to the music, with

their arms in the air and plenty of jumping. I managed a gentle swaying motion, but was too distracted by thoughts of what I was going to say to Nick. Luckily I didn't need to worry too much. He was so high from adrenaline when he got off stage that he talked enough for all of us.

He told me that my ex-classmate was now a councillor for their local area, which I was chuffed about until he said what party he represented. 'I never knew he was a selfish prick,' I said, causing Nick to laugh so hard he spat beer out.

'How about you?' Nick asked. I told him that I was now a teacher, and he looked at me with respect. 'I could never do that,' he said. 'I remember how awful I was to teachers.'

'They keep me on my toes,' I admitted. Not that any of my students had led a mass student walkout, as Nick once had, claiming that it was too warm inside to study and insisted that his classmates would only meet in the pub from then on.

The bar staff had started collecting glasses and most of the crowd had departed when the music had finished. Matt went to use the bathroom and Nick asked me for my mobile number. 'I was thinking maybe I could look you up? For old times' sake?' he asked, and winked at me. I handed him my mobile to enter his number in and I promised to text him.

I was just thinking about how I could meet up with him somewhere more private and subtly find out what had gone wrong, when Matt returned. I took my chance to use the loos, Charmaine was right about not using the ones back at Matt's house if you could help it. I had once discovered that his flatmate had been tasked to clean it before my parents visited. He'd opened a window and hidden the porn mags and been pleased that he'd done a thorough job. It had smelt so bad I'd almost been sick.

When I got back to the table Charmaine was rolling

her eyes at something one of the guys had said, and they all stood as I approached, ready to leave. We bid our goodbyes and began walking back to the house, but two minutes later I realised I'd forgotten my jacket.

'The front bar will still be open while they re-stock for tomorrow,' Matt said.

'I'm not going in,' Charmaine said.

Matt teased her about being scared, and whilst she refused to admit it, she would not budge. Instead I knocked on the door and was let in by myself to look for it. I wandered round the side of the small bar and out towards the stage. So far so good, as I didn't see any ghosts, but I did hear a clatter behind me and jumped out of my skin. Realising that it was just two people making out behind the bar, I relaxed until they broke apart and I saw that one of them was Nick.

'Just came to get my coat,' I said, picking it up from the table and backing away.

Though I hadn't thought about him in a long time until that week, it still hurt to think that he'd been chatting me up only ten minutes before I caught him snogging the barmaid. I blinked tears out of my eyes and tried to pull myself together again before I went back outside.

'Got it,' I said, holding up my jacket. I led the way down the street and they had to jog to catch up with me.

'Slow down,' my cousin panted. 'I've got heels on and I can't run.'

I did as she asked, but even once they'd caught me I found it hard to concentrate on their chatter. It wasn't until I heard Charmaine moaning at Matt for being overprotective that I zoned back in again. 'What did you say?' I asked.

'I was giving him a bollocking for warning Nick off you,' she said.

'Warning Nick off me?' I asked, my voice rising despite how late at night it was and how many houses lined the street we were on.

Charmaine put her hand on my arm to try and calm me down but I shrugged it off. A light flicked on in a room opposite where we stood but no one emerged from the houses. I tried to get my temper back under control.

'I just pointed out that you were my little sister and he should be careful,' Matt said, as if in my mid-twenties I still needed his protection.

'You do realise that thanks to your little warning he had already decided not to bother with me at all,' I said, and turning my back on them, I carried on walking.

'What happened?' Charmaine asked.

I stopped and turned back to face them.

'By the time I went back in just now he had already moved on to the barmaid.'

'See, so it's just as well I warned him off, save you getting hurt by someone who would cheat on you,' my brother said.

'Or maybe he would have been okay but he thought that it wasn't worth bothering with someone who still turned up to gigs with their bodyguard.'

Back at Matt's house I was fuming with him. I think he knew because he gave up his bed without complaint so that Charmaine and I could share it and took himself off to sleep on the sofa.

'So who's next?' Charmaine asked.

'Maybe I should give up on this whole bloody scheme,' I said, trying not to cry. 'So far all it has reminded me is that my taste in men is awful, and that even when I find a cute guy he can't be bothered with me.'

'Or maybe it's shown you that the people you were choosing were either not good enough or not grown up enough to handle you. Didn't Nick start going out with one of Matt's many exes just after he dumped you? Maybe he just wanted someone he thought would be a surer thing back then too?' she countered. 'So who is next?'

'I think I'll skip the next one, I have no idea how I'll go about it.'

'So who was it?' she asked again, turning over in bed and accidentally kneeing me in the back.

'It was the first time I kissed George,' I admitted.

Chapter Seven

It was the summer that I'd turned seventeen. Matt was two years older, and after his year out, which he'd spent partially travelling but mostly going out drinking and partying with George, he was off to university. He'd arranged a meal with some friends for the night before he left. I was never sure whether my parents had guilt-tripped him into inviting me, or whether he'd felt sorry for me sitting at home yet again as he went out, but I was a last minute addition to the group.

We'd had a private room at the back of a restaurant. My parents had paid for the food but we were paying for our own drinks, so I spent most of the evening slowly nursing my pint. Matt had had a few, and after we'd finished eating he suggested that we move next door to where the bar had a dance floor.

I followed them through, but hung back and watched as Matt asked several girls in turn to dance. They all said yes, of course, and I admired his confidence. One of his mates asked me to dance, and I was about to join in, when another guy led him off to the bar instead, so I sat back down and carried on watching everyone else having fun.

Eventually it was kicking out time. The other girls shared a cab home, and the guys gradually wandered off in different directions. By the time we got back to our house, it was only Matt, George and I left. We went in and I put the kettle on to make us some tea. I figured Matt could probably use some time to sober up. He started a film, but within ten minutes was fast asleep on the sofa. I got up and fetched a blanket to cover him.

'He's going to feel rough tomorrow,' George said with a grin. I smiled back, but only for a moment.

George took my hand and led me into the kitchen. I wasn't sure what he was thinking but I followed him anyway.

'What's up?' he asked me. 'Didn't you have fun tonight?'

'I did,' I assured him. 'It was nice to watch you all.'

'I noticed that you didn't join in. Don't you like dancing?'

'I do. I just, well, no one asked me,' I said, wondering why I hadn't just danced by myself as some of the others had. I wondered whether he would laugh at how shy I suddenly felt, but instead he reached out and drew me against him.

'We can dance now,' he said, resting his hands on my hips and moving me against him.

I looked up at him, and he returned the eye contact. Neither of us blinked, and he ran his fingers slowly down my face.

'This is a little confusing,' he said.

'What is?' I asked, still unable to take my eyes off him. He slowly lowered his head until he could place a gentle kiss on my lips.

Even though I hadn't seen it coming, as soon as he touched me it felt electric, and I found myself stood on my tiptoes kissing him back. He wrapped me in his arms, and I crushed myself against him, returning his kisses with a passion and an energy that surprised me. He stepped back, and I took his hand and led him to the counter. Lifting myself up until I was sat on it, I was the same height as him now and I reached for him. Wrapping my legs around his waist, I drew him in and kissed him again until we both needed to come up for air.

'Wow,' he said, stepping back and running his hands through his hair.

'That was fun,' I said, trying to act grown up and not show him that my legs were actually shaking like jelly. It was lucky that I was sat down. He kissed me again, and I let my hands reach down and run over his backside. It felt hard and muscular below my fingers. I could feel a bulge pressing against me, and I wondered how far he would take this. I wasn't sure myself how far I was ready to go. He lifted my blouse, and was just stroking my back and reaching for my bra strap when we heard the living room door shut. He jumped back, and we both straightened our clothes.

Matt walked in, and I pretended that we'd just come in to get another drink and got chatting. Matt said he was going to bed, and he guided George towards the front door. I wanted to offer to show him out, I was desperate for one more goodnight kiss, or maybe to ask him where it had come from, but there was no opportunity and before I knew it he had gone. I didn't see him again for three months after that, until Matt came home at Christmas.

By that point I had got over him, and developed a crush on a boy in my psychology class, but it all changed when George got me under the mistletoe. Matt had got lucky at the club and gone home with a pretty blonde girl. When he'd asked George to make sure I got home safely, I don't think Matt realised what he was doing.

As soon as Matt disappeared George had taken my hand and kissed it. He put a smile on my face and a lot of questions in my mind. Of course I didn't ask him any of them. I was too scared that if I did I wouldn't like the answers, so I walked home through the snow, holding his arm and following his lead. Mum had hung some mistletoe above our door. I'm not sure who she meant it for. Matt and I made throwing up noises whenever she got my dad under it.

George though looked up, smiled, and without a word kissed me until I was breathless again. I opened the door and dragged him inside. Pushing him onto the sofa, I climbed on top of him and kissed him until he laid me down and started unbuttoning my blouse. As he undid my bra, I came to my senses and sat back.

'I think we need to stop,' I said, pulling away. He kissed my neck and ran his fingers across the lace of my bra.

'If you're sure,' he muttered, nibbling my collarbone. I kissed him again, and he slipped a finger into the waistband of my skirt, reaching for the zip. I pushed his hand away and stood up.

'No, I really do need to stop,' I said, panting hard. It was the furthest I'd ever gone, and though I loved how he felt pressed against me, I had neither the confidence to test what we'd do next, nor the will to follow through without knowing whether I would see George again afterwards if I did.

He got up and straightened his clothes, not that he could disguise the fact that his trousers would no longer lie flat. He blew out a sigh. I let him out, he kissed me goodbye but didn't say another word. I wondered what on earth I had been thinking. Maybe I'd just been enjoying myself. Maybe that was okay. What wasn't okay was the way I felt about myself the next day, when I began to feel lost, not knowing whether his lack of communication was because he was annoyed with me for leading him on and then stopping, though I had every right to, or anger at myself for letting him react in that way without calling him out for it. I swore off him, and this time held to my word for six months before I'd fallen under his spell once more.

So I was in no rush to visit him to continue tracking down my past. I wasn't sure whether I was more angry with myself that I had fallen for him repeatedly over the years, or whether I was pissed at him for spotting when I was vulnerable and taking his chances. Regardless, given that we had been destined to reconnect several more times over the next few years, I told myself I wasn't chickening out by saving that task for the future.

Charmaine let out a gentle snore, and I turned over and tried to copy her, but my mind wandered back to the next man in my little black book.

Chapter Eight

Wandering around a craft store in town, I found the resources I needed for my class the next day. I'd wanted to find a range of card so that my kids could take inspiration from different styles of decorative papers to make covers for diaries and books, to see how it affected their writing. I filled my basket and headed towards the cash desk to pay.

Where in a supermarket they have chocolates and sweets to tempt you into making impulse purchases, these tills were surrounded by beautiful craft kits to entice you to make your own candles or stained glass panels. They had a home baking set that had a cute yellow apron and chef's hat inside. The girl in the picture on the box had curly hair just like Alice, and I found myself adding it to my basket too.

Afterwards, I wasn't sure why I'd bought it. I hoped Bea wouldn't think I was odd dropping round a gift for a child I hardly knew, but once I'd paid for the box there was no point in keeping it. I knocked on the door and Jake let me in. He seemed pleased to see me at least, and I stopped feeling so silly.

'Come in,' he said, stepping back so I could enter.

'I saw this and thought of Alice,' I said, handing over my purchase.

'That's really kind, thank you. Alice will be so excited, though I'm not sure Bea will want me helping her to bake again any time soon.'

I grinned, and he touched my arm and pointed to a chair. 'Fancy a glass of wine? Bea might be a little while still. I accidentally let Alice have a nap this afternoon and she was still bouncing when she went up. I'm not sure I'm in their good books right now.'

'I'm sure you are in Alice's, if not your sister's.'

He laughed. I asked how Jake's job-hunting was going, and he told me about the design firms he had sent his CV to that week. Half a glass of wine later Bea came downstairs. She looked exhausted. 'Uncle Jake, Alice is still awake and is now asking for you.'

'I'll head off,' I said, standing up too.

'You don't have to go,' Bea said, as Jake showed her the gift I'd brought. 'I've been reading *The Very Hungry Caterpillar* on repeat for the last half an hour and I would love some company while I have a glass of wine. In fact, I plan to have two, and it would feel sociable rather than an unhealthy coping technique if you were to join me.'

I accepted her kind offer.

'I promise I'll try not to let her nap tomorrow,' Jake said, grinning and heading upstairs to take a shift.

'He's a great uncle,' I commented.

'He really is, even though today is going to be such a late night for her. I've been glad to have him around at the moment, that's for sure.' She topped up our wine and showed me into the living room. We curled up on her sofa, and she told me a bit more about her divorce. It sounded like she was still in shock, though Alice seemed to be coping remarkably well. I guess having her uncle around for distraction was probably helping with that.

'How about you? Are you seeing anyone?' she asked me.

I shook my head. 'No. Nope. No way.'

'That's a pretty strong reaction,' she remarked.

'I've come to realise recently that I've had a few lucky escapes in the past. I've decided not to date for a while until I get things a bit straighter in my own mind,' I explained.

Bea wanted to know what I meant, and I found myself telling her about the challenge I'd set myself. I wasn't sure why I was opening up so much to her, but at the same time I couldn't stop myself talking. Perhaps it was the wine. Perhaps we both needed a friend, because Bea seemed to talk as freely as I did, and I wasn't sure this was her usual approach either. 'I hope that by the time I work my way back through my dating history, I'll have more of a sense of why I'm still single, and why the guys that I have been interested in have all ended up being utter plonkers.'

'If you get any answers please do let me know,' she replied. 'I'd quite like to find out what happened in my marriage too.' She poured the last of the bottle into our glasses. It had disappeared all too quickly, and I explained the reason why I'd originally knocked on her door, and how quickly I'd run from the butcher's shop once I'd set eyes on Bill Banks.

'So who will you be looking up next?' she asked.

I didn't want to explain about skipping over George, so instead I told her about the trip I was thinking of making. 'I don't have any way of contacting the next guy on my list. Truthfully, I'm not entirely sure that I even spelt his name correctly in my book.'

'So what are you going to do to find him?' Bea said, resting her head against a cushion.

'I thought that perhaps instead of looking up the guy himself, I'd go back to where I met him and see how I feel once I get there.'

'And where is that?'

'Dublin,' I said, with determination. Charmaine had looked at me like I was crazy when I had told her my plan. Even though she supported me, she wasn't sure that the expense of travelling to Ireland would help me feel more at peace.

'I thought I'd visit my family, and go back to a few of the places that I visited when I was a teenager, try and recapture that youthful energy,' I said. 'My gran and quite a few of my cousins still live there.'

Bea looked pensive. 'I can imagine how it might feel to go back to a more carefree time. Sometimes I can't quite believe how my life has turned out. Ted and I were together for so long. I never thought I'd end up as a single mum. But I wouldn't swap Alice for the world so I wouldn't go back and change my past, even if I could.'

'Oh, I'm not after changing the past,' I assured her, 'or even reliving it. I want to learn from it. I got engaged last year but we'd split up within six months.' I spared her any more details about how unpleasant that experience had been. 'I don't know why my previous relationships haven't worked but I don't want to spend the rest of my life on my own. So, next weekend I'll be flying to Dublin.'

'Dublin?' said a voice behind me. I turned and saw Jake standing in the doorway.

'I sang to her and she fell asleep,' he told Bea. She looked relieved to know that Alice was down and that she wasn't going to have to deal with an over-tired and cranky toddler tomorrow. 'Yup, I started off with ninety-nine green bottles hanging on a wall, she was asleep by the time I got down to the last four bottles. I finished the song though, I don't like to leave a job half done.'

Jake winked at me, and I felt butterflies in my stomach. Where had those come from? I took a mouthful of wine and hoped it would settle them.

'What did I miss?' he asked.

'Evie was just telling me that she's going to Dublin next weekend,' Bea told him.

'I've never been, always wanted to go. There's a fantastic modern art museum,' he said, sitting next to me.

The sofa was small and dipped under his weight so that I ended up pressed against him. I picked my glass up and swallowed the rest of the wine. 'It would be useful for me, actually. There's a piece I wanted to look at, I've got something based on it in my portfolio but I've only ever seen photographs of it. You don't mind if I come too, do you?'

How could I say no to that?

Chapter Nine

'Thanks for letting me come along,' Jake said, as he put his elbow on my armrest.

'No problem,' I told him, though truthfully I still felt slightly thrown that we had arranged for him to come with me. I blamed the wine. Charmaine had been hoping to come too, but at the last minute she'd been called in to work all weekend. Her team was catering a huge event and she was likely to be running herself ragged whipping up gourmet meals for a hundred people. And to top it off, we'd been planning to stay with my gran, and Jake, having little extra cash to spare whilst he was unemployed, seemed to think that this was open to him too. I hadn't had the heart to say no. So now Jake and I were sat on the plane, eating tasteless sandwiches that we'd bought in the duty free. I tried not to remember how it had felt to be sliding into him on the sofa.

Jake read through his guidebook, pointing at every other page to a place he wanted to visit. He was so excited to see the museum of modern art it was like being next to a kid

'We've only got two days,' I reminded him.

'We'll have to walk quickly, pack a lot in,' he said, turning the page and showing me another place of interest.

'I'm not sure you've got the hang of Ireland,' I said, smiling. 'My plan is to drop our bags off at my gran's so we get a chance to spend a couple of hours with her, then go into the city to tour the Guinness museum, and if you still feel like walking a lot after that, then you've not had enough of their wares.'

Jake laughed, and I found myself smiling at him

again. He kept reading the guidebook but he stopped pointing pages out to me. I closed my eyes and sat back, daydreaming about the trip that Charmaine and I had taken nine years before.

I'd been so fed up after kissing George, again, and hearing nothing from him, again, that I'd persuaded my dad to pay for a trip for us both to visit our gran so that we could get away. I'd wanted to know that I was going to have a few days where I ran no chance of bumping into him in the street. Dad was happy that Gran would have some company from our branch of the family and it meant that he could save his trip home to see her at Christmas, so he agreed. We were young enough that the chance to travel on our own felt exciting, even though the flight itself was only a little over an hour and we'd spent half of our holidays there as kids.

We'd spent most of our trip visiting aunties and uncles and being fed and given endless cups of tea. On our last day we'd pleaded for a few hours to sightsee, we'd walked by the river and followed the trail of tourists until we'd ended up at the Guinness museum.

Charmaine had been fascinated by the machinery, the tanks and the mechanisation that had crept into the production. I was grabbed by the history, and the photographs of the people who had made the drink famous. We both agreed that the museum was amazing, made perfect by the bar that sat at the top of the glass-shaped building, with a view that looked out over the old factory.

We'd stopped up there for a couple of drinks, and Charmaine soon caught the eye of a gorgeous bloke who was hitchhiking round the country as he wrote his PhD about Irish folk music. He'd sung to her in the bar, bringing the room to silence and melting her instantly.

When he finished she led him to the corner and started snogging him. I'd sat on my own with my drink for half an hour before another young man took pity on me and came over for a chat. I'd made him laugh with stories of scrapes that Charmaine and I had got up to before, and after a couple more pints and an hour of us chatting, sat pressed against each other in the busy bar, I plucked up the courage to lean forward and kiss him.

We both knew it was just a quick holiday flirtation. Neither of us made any mention of swapping mobile numbers or email addresses. There wasn't really any way that I would re-connect with him just by going back to Dublin, but I felt the call to go to my roots, and hoped that by going back I might find a taste of the courage that had led me to lean forward and make the first move for the first time. It had felt like an intoxicating power, even though I never felt able to wield it as surely as my cousin did.

The flight was bumpy. Jake grinned like a little boy but I had to stop myself holding onto his hand as we landed. My cousin Aiden picked us up from the airport and drove us back to my gran's house. Aiden's hair was the same vivid ginger as mine, but he had his hidden by a baseball cap labelled with his favourite football team. He'd spotted Jake's Arsenal T-shirt under his jacket and spent most of the journey teasing him about their dire season. I sat looking out of the window, feeling that I was both coming home, yet still feeling lost at the same time.

My gran's two up, two down house was as filled with knick-knacks on every surface, lace doilies and pictures of various saints as it had ever been. I wondered whether she'd expect us to go to mass with her the next morning and hoped she didn't ask how long it was since I'd last been to confession. I thought her favourite priest would have had a heart attack if he'd read all the details I'd recorded in my notebook.

My gran fussed over us, feeding us tea and her home-made soda bread. She fetched old photo albums and embarrassed me by showing Jake the books from the trip when I'd been three and going through a phase of refusing to wear many clothes. I decided it was lucky that he'd been spending some time with his niece and understood the strong opinions held by small children, otherwise he might worry that I was crazy. Instead he seemed completely at ease, chatting with my cousins and hearing all about my childhood holidays.

It was me who was growing restless, stuck inside my gran's small house with the net curtains and too many cushions. When she commented on what a lovely couple Jake and I made, I hurriedly corrected her, then announced that we were going out to do some sightseeing. We had two hours left before the Guinness museum closed, so we decided to go straight there.

Jake read every noticeboard and studied every photograph on display, and I grew irritable waiting for him to finish up and come up to the bar. I tried to distract myself by looking at the old photographs that had intrigued me so on my previous visit, but today I could hardly concentrate.

Eventually Jake gave up looking around and announced that I must be truly desperate for a pint to be quite so antsy all the way around the museum. I led him upstairs where we found that with only half an hour left before closing, the bar was packed. There were no seats, and we were pressed up against each other as we ordered our drinks.

Jake carried our glasses and threaded his way through the crowd until he came to a quiet corner, the same one where Charmaine had spent the afternoon snogging her singer last time. He clinked my glass and said, 'Slainte.'

I took a deep swallow, and felt the black liquid cool and soothe my churning stomach.

'This is a good pint,' Jake said, wiping foam from his lips.

'Well, if they didn't know how to pour it correctly here they'd be in trouble,' I pointed out.

Jake took another drink and set his glass down on the ledge next to us. 'Are you going to tell me what's really going on now?' he asked.

'I have no idea what you're talking about,' I blustered.

'Come on,' he said. 'You've been wound tighter than a spring since we got here. I might not know you very well yet, but this doesn't seem like the woman who had endless patience with an incompetent cook and an energetic child.'

I took a deep drink from my glass and decided to tell him about my plan. Bea had understood, and it might be nice to get a guy's perspective on where I was going wrong. I made a second trip to the bar though first to give me a little more time. Plus hopefully the alcohol would help give me the courage to open up.

'So you've flown all the way over here because when you were eighteen you kissed a guy at the bar, even though you knew you wouldn't see him here again?' Jake said, after I had explained. 'I thought you were coming to visit your gran?'

'I have come to visit her too,' I said, feeling a little self-centred now that I had revealed the main reason for my trip.

'And how do you feel now that you're here?' Jake asked.

'I don't know,' I admitted. 'I don't think I have the same self-assurance I had then. I can't imagine making the first move and kissing a guy at the moment.'

A lady, who was standing behind Jake, moved her bag, knocking into him and pressing him against me. 'Why

57

not?' he asked, tucking a flyaway strand of hair behind my ear. 'You're beautiful.'

I laughed and pretended that my heart wasn't beating at a million miles an hour. He leant forward and kissed me, gently and sweetly, on the lips. 'There. Now you can go home knowing that you've remembered how attractive you are,' he said.

'I didn't make the first move. Last time I had the confidence to kiss him. It's been a while since I felt able to do that without worrying that I was misreading the signs.'

'Then kiss me first,' Jake suggested. 'I don't mind, if it'll help you with your mission I mean.'

He smiled, and for a moment I forgot how many people were crowded around us. I forgot all the men I'd met before and, most importantly, I forgot all those who came after. Leaning forward, I kissed Jake, just for the briefest of moments, and it felt perfect.

Leaning back, he lifted his glass and took a long gulp. Perhaps the attraction had thrown him as much as it had thrown me. I smiled but felt my eyes were filling up and I had to blink so that the tears wouldn't fall. The lady behind us pushed into Jake again, and he took my arm. 'Let's go home,' he said.

Chapter Ten

We didn't kiss again that weekend. Instead I acted like the perfect tour guide, putting my moodiness aside and ensuring that Jake saw the staggeringly beautiful cathedrals and botanic gardens that he'd read about in his guidebook. He spent so long in the Museum of Modern Art I began to fear that they would lock us in for the night, and too soon it was time to head home. On the return flight I was sure at one point that Jake was about to ask me something personal, so I closed my eyes and pretended to be asleep until he looked away.

Back home, we gave Alice a teddy bear covered in shamrocks, and Bea a bottle of whiskey. They both looked pleased with their gifts. Jake walked me to the door, and I wished him a goodnight and thanked him for his company. He leant forward to kiss my cheek, but I turned my head at the same time to kiss his and our lips accidentally brushed.

'Sorry,' I said, pulling back.

'There's no need to be sorry,' he assured me.

'You're a really lovely guy,' I told him, 'but I need to finish my task before I start anything new. I need to understand what I've been doing, so that I don't make any more mistakes.'

'I do understand. It's okay, this thing, whatever this is with us, it's taken me by surprise too,' he said, laying his hand gently on my waist. 'I wasn't looking for anything right now either. There's too much in my life that is unsettled; not having a job, being here to help Bea and Alice.'

I went to step back and give him some more personal space, as this seemed to be what he was asking for, but he reached out and drew me back in for a hug. 'I'm not ready to walk away though, and I don't know what to do. I don't want to be another bloke who messes you around.'

'I don't think you could be,' I assured him. 'But for me, for now, I need to do this,' I told him.

He blew out a sigh. 'How about I help you so that you can be done quicker? Then at least one of us will know what we're doing.'

I grinned and told him to pack his dancing shoes. 'Next weekend we're going back to university.'

Charmaine wasn't working the following Friday, so I booked us some rooms in a cheap hotel on the outskirts of Nottingham, and the three of us drove up in my Mini after I finished work.

'How many bags did you need for one night?' Jake asked, pressed up against my suitcase on the back seat. His head nearly brushed the ceiling, and his feet were pushed against the back of my chair. The car fit me perfectly, but having two tall companions on this trip I was reminded that this wasn't true for everyone.

'I found a bag of my old clothes from when we used to go clubbing. I didn't have time to sort out which ones I can still imagine wearing so I brought the whole lot. Then I needed a range of shoes depending on which clothes I pick.'

'Of course you did,' he muttered, and I guessed that the only shoes he'd brought were the ones already on his feet.

'So what's the plan?' Charmaine asked. 'Please don't tell me we're going back to the Student Union bar? I spent enough time drinking watered down beer when I used to come and visit you.'

'I've decided to condense reliving the first year of university with one trip to the nightclub I used to go to.

None of the guys I met then made much of an emotional impact so I think we can safely skip looking each and every one up.' I glanced back at Jake in the rear-view mirror. He had a subtle smile, I almost missed it with my quick glimpse at him, and I wondered whether it was at my admittance that none of the guys had been very important to me. 'It will be a bit different tonight, we used to come on a Tuesday which was student night,' I continued, looking back at the road again. 'Tonight it'll be more locals there, but I wanted to remember how it felt to be here, carefree and with a group of mates.'

'Sounds good to me,' Charmaine said.

We checked in at the hotel. Jake had a room to himself, which was small but functional. Charmaine and I were sharing a twin room.

'I'm going to get changed,' Jake said as he helped carry bags to our room. 'Shall I knock back for you in twenty minutes?' Charmaine laughed at his optimism. 'I've brought a book, how about you knock on my door once you're ready?' he suggested.

We took it in turns to shower and my cousin helped apply my make-up. She painted my lips with her bright red lipstick. 'Are you sure this doesn't clash with my hair?' I asked her.

'If you look confident you'll be able to act confident,' she assured me.

I started lifting outfits from my bag. 'This was stuffed at the back of my wardrobe,' I told her. 'I haven't looked in here in years.'

'That's the outfit,' she said as I held up two small pieces of fabric. I wasn't convinced, but I tried them on anyway and she wouldn't let me get changed. I could hardly bear to look at myself in the mirror in our room and wished that I had a baggy shirt to cover up with. Charmaine was adamant though; we were here to relive our youth and that included dressing the part. When we knocked on Jake's door he couldn't take his eyes off me, which was even more surprising and flattering when you're stood next to another lady who is five foot nine and has curves usually only achieved with enormous quantities of silicone.

'I think this is a bit out of style now,' I said, trying to explain my outfit. 'It was all about backless tops when I was here, and I'm flat chested enough to get away without needing a bra so I can wear them.'

'You're petite and in proportion,' Charmaine assured me.

Jake nodded his approval. He didn't speak, but as he was still staring at me, he didn't need to and I started to relax.

'Still, I'm not sure how I used to go out in this skirt without anything on underneath.' At that Jake began to make choking noises and I realised what I'd said. I tripped over my words as I tried to clarify what I'd meant. 'Tights. Without tights on or leggings.' Today I'd chickened out and had teamed my black miniskirt with some leggings. Jake nodded but still I found that he positioned himself at my side as we left the hotel.

We called a cab and took it into the city centre. 'Shall we try your old local first?' Charmaine suggested. 'It's a bit too early to hit the club yet.'

We settled in at a table at the back, and I tried in vain to tug my skirt down lower as I sat. I must have been far braver in my teens than I was now.

'So who are we re-living this evening?' Jake asked.

'I got a bit brave in my first year, or perhaps just a bit drunk, so tonight we'll be harking back to the student experience of watered down lager, alco pops, and snogging on the dance floor,' I told them, trying hard not to catch his eye as I said it. 'I didn't really date anyone properly in my first year, but I did rack up a few random snogs. There was Javier, the exchange student, plus Phil from my classics module, Nate from historical literature, and that guy that I met the night of the rugby ball. Oh, also the Valentine's Day event, Elliot, I think his name was, and Joe, at the end of term bash.'

'So quite a few guys then,' Jake said, lifting his pint to hide his grin.

I was glad that I had skipped telling him about how I'd also hooked up with George several times that year too. Reading back through my notebook, it had charted each rise and fall of my feelings for him. Each time I'd felt confident about myself as a woman, I'd go home, dress in something skimpy, hang out somewhere that I knew I'd see him and enjoy seeing the effect it had on him. It felt like a victory too, the first time I'd taken the lead on flirting with him when it had worked and he had gone home with me. Likewise, when I'd had a knock back, for example when Nate had been the first man to formally dump me to go out with a girl who I thought was not very attractive, I'd invited Matt to stay for a few days, and, of course, George had come too.

Emotionally, Nate had had minimal impact on me, but that was probably because I knew I had the back-up option of exploring my sexuality with George. As soon as Matt had hooked up and gone home with someone I'd dragged George back to my halls room and this time I'd let him slip my bra off. I wasn't being uncharitable about the girl I got dumped for either. When I pointed her out to Matt he had physically grimaced, and Matt wasn't exactly picky. It was nice to know George had still found me attractive.

'I think covering all of those guys in one night sounds pretty sensible, otherwise we'd be here every weekend for months,' Charmaine said, sipping her glass of wine. She'd refused to start drinking the over sweet and highly alcoholic bottles that I was drinking as a throwback to the past until we got to the club.

Once there, the queue reached around the block, and I'd remembered why I rarely went clubbing any more. By the time we got in, the cloudless blue sky we'd had all day had given way to a cool evening. I was decidedly chilly in places that I didn't want to moan about out loud. I wondered how we'd come out wearing so little even in the middle of winter. I wished that I'd been able to wear a bra with my top and hoped I'd warm up before I took someone's eye out.

'I'm realising why you had such a successful year,' Jake whispered in my ear, and I used my finger to raise his face until he was again looking at my eyes. 'Sorry,' he said. 'I am only human.'

I laughed, and found confidence in his attention. He never made me feel uncomfortable, instead his occasional glances and the accompanying smiles left me feeling safe and admired. I didn't need another drink after that and instead led the way to the dance floor.

'So are you trying to hook up with a random tonight to help you relive old times?' Charmaine asked.

I hadn't told her about kissing Jake in Dublin. I knew she wouldn't be able to resist teasing us, and I wanted to have some time without any additional pressure to work out my growing feelings for him.

'No, I'm trying to have fun, and remember how it feels not to be nervous,' I told her.

We danced until our feet ached. Jake stayed by my side all evening, but whenever it felt too intense I'd turn away and dance with my cousin instead. He didn't offer to be my surrogate kiss as he had in Dublin, and by the end of the night I wasn't sure if I was relieved or upset by that.

Chapter Eleven

I felt invigorated by the dancing and the attention, and returned to school ready to engage and enthuse my class. Unfortunately they had the end of term feeling already and were sat slumped across their desks.

'This passage is beautiful,' I told them, reading aloud from my copy of *Romeo and Juliet*. 'Don't you feel stirred by the emotion and passion of their feelings for one another?'

Twenty-five blank faces looked back at me. I finally had the attention of all but the one kid who was fast asleep at the back. I balled up a piece of paper and threw it at him. He woke up with a jerk and looked at me, but I carried on as if nothing had happened and he sat there looking confused.

'They both end up dead so wasn't it a bit stupid, miss?' said a voice at the back.

I tried to use this to springboard a discussion about whether they'd had any choice but to follow their feelings, but my class were reluctant to agree with me.

'I wouldn't risk my life for no man,' Zoe said, kissing her teeth.

'That's lucky 'cos there ain't no man brave enough to go near you,' shouted Daniel.

'All right, calm down class,' I told them, trying to quiet the laughter as Zoe glared at him. I felt their attention slipping away again as the room went still.

'How do you think it felt to them, to be teenagers in love but be barred by their parents from seeing each other? How would you feel if your parents stood in the way of you going near people you fancied?' I asked them. A couple of heads perked up and I saw a little more interest on their faces, finally, just as the bell rang and they grabbed their bags and moved on to the next class.

I had a free period and followed them out into the hall. Locking my classroom, I walked up to the staffroom to make myself a cuppa. I had the year sevens next, the youngest year group in the school, and it would take all my energy to keep them concentrating for the whole lesson.

I set them off writing a letter in a bottle, as if they were trying to contact people when stuck on a desert island. A few kids got stuck in, and wrote detailed instructions on how to find and rescue them. One boy wrote a shopping list of all the items he wanted sending to him, including his games console and a laptop. I wasn't entirely sure he'd understood the premise of being stranded with no creature comforts, including electricity.

Finally the bell rang signalling the end of the day. Once the kids had gone home and the playground was empty, I walked around my room straightening chairs and throwing away scraps of paper. I found myself wondering who I would write to, if I was stranded. Would I ever fall in love and be able to give myself and risk everything as completely as the star-crossed lovers had? If I did, would it go as tragically wrong for me as it had for them? Would my past experiences continue to hold me back? I hoped that my undertaking would give me the confidence and understanding to ensure that it did not.

An image of Jake floated into my mind, and I blinked it away. There was no doubt that I cared about him, but I didn't want to hook up with him quickly only for it all to fall to pieces again. He felt too special to risk that with and so I was determined to wait until I had more answers. Instead, I tried to concentrate on the meal I was going to make that evening. Charmaine was coming over again and we were going to think about the next challenge: how to track down my first serious boyfriend.

I'd met Rob in my second year at university, when I'd been roped in as a spare body for medical students to practise their examinations on. Luckily there had been no restrictions on medical students dating their fake patients. He'd spent an hour with me in the hall set aside for their practical tests, checking my pulse and my blood pressure and rotating various parts of my body. I'd lain back and enjoyed the feel of his hands on me. When he had asked if I had any questions, I'd amazed myself by asking him if he wanted to go for a drink with me. We'd spent a few weeks having fun examining each other after that in more intimate surroundings.

By then I was living in a shared house with three other girls, and whilst they had all had guys staying overnight, I hadn't yet. I'd never been in a rush to lose my virginity, but neither did I have any plans to wait until I was married. I was a firm believer in making sure that you knew you were compatible, in all areas before tying the knot, rather than after. When I was sixteen I'd decided to wait until I fell in love before I slept with anyone, and that didn't happen. When I was seventeen I thought it would be nice to wait until I found someone I really deeply cared for. This also didn't come to pass. By the time I was eighteen, I thought I'd wait until it felt right and, with Rob, when I was nineteen, it finally did.

My little black book had noted: *'I think I may have found someone special. I met Rob last week and we've already been out for a drink three times. He's so nice, really thoughtful. He turned up with a bar of chocolate yesterday because he knew I'd been stressing about an exam. It's weird, I've been looking forward to meeting someone like him so for long, someone who actually seems to really like me, I don't really know how to handle it. Maybe I'll just try and relax and enjoy it, if I can.'*

I wasn't in love with him, but we were spending lots of time together, and each time we went out we'd come back to my room afterwards and go just a little bit further. He was the first man that I saw naked, and it was fun exploring and getting comfortable with each other's bodies. We'd been going out for about six weeks when I decided it was time.

I bought myself a slinky black nightie, and a box of extra-safe condoms. I didn't tell Rob that I was prepared just in case I changed my mind, but I put my purchases in the small cabinet next to my bed and started to get excited. One night after a medics ball Rob asked if he could stay over. I thought about my secret stash and told him that he could, but then Mother Nature intervened and I got my period. It turned out that the combination of alcohol, mixed messages, hormones and exam stress was a toxic cocktail. We ended up having one of those stupid fights, filled with angry words but not really about anything in particular.

We didn't speak for a week, and it hurt because I'd thought he was the one. The following Saturday I packed a bag, went home for the weekend, and, after Matt had gone to bed, I sneaked George up to my room and slept with him. It hadn't been the romantic experience I'd been hoping for. He was gentle with me, and kept asking to make sure it was what I wanted to do, but I didn't feel moved by it. Especially when shortly after we'd finished he'd got dressed, dropped a quick kiss on my forehead and left. Afterwards I felt like I'd cheated myself, given up on my hopes for making love for the first time to be a special event.

I got back to university to find a note from Rob apologising, but I wasn't sure how to explain my actions, so although we had a coffee together and made our peace, we never did go out again. He said he hadn't meant to be pissed off when we had argued. He'd only reacted when I'd yelled at him and he'd argued back but he hadn't meant what he'd said. I didn't know how to tell him that I'd effectively cheated on him, so I just said that maybe we weren't that well-suited after all, and we went our separate ways. A few weeks later I saw him making out with another medical student so I guess I hadn't hurt him too badly after all.

I didn't want to remember how cheap I'd felt when I realised that I'd messed up my best opportunity so far to go out with a man properly, one who had actually cared about me. I'd spent months questioning my choices back then. My notebook was a testament to the confusion, with whole chapters devoted to how good it could have been with Rob if I hadn't broken up with him. Then there were the other sections, trying to justify why I'd hooked up with George. Even though we'd never made a commitment to each other I had adored him.

Looking back I was surprised at what I'd written. I'd remembered how attracted to George I'd been, and the strength of the friendship we'd built up over the years that I'd known him. I'd forgotten though how angry I'd felt at him afterwards for never ringing me, especially when Rob and I had finally talked and it became more evident what I'd thrown away. It was strange to see the emotions that had been so keen at the time, played out in my own handwriting. It was as though the feelings had belonged to another person, they were so long ago and far away from how I felt now, but wasn't that the point? To recapture the feeling of being free to fall for someone again?

Would looking Rob up just remind me of how easily I'd run away from him last time? I'd set myself the challenge though, and skipping over the parts of my history that I was most uncomfortable about wouldn't help me understand myself any better.

I googled his name, and found that he had a private clinic in London, offering cosmetic surgery consults. There was a small photo of Rob, wearing his white coat, glasses and a stethoscope and looking very professional. It was a far cry from when I'd last seen him, dressed in ripped jeans and a T-shirt depicting his favourite heavy metal band. His ponytail was gone, replaced by a shorter, slicked back look. It showed off his cheekbones and, if anything, he looked better now than he had back then.

I sent Charmaine a link to his website, and wasn't surprised when an hour later my front door opened as she let herself in ready to make battle plans. 'How about you book an appointment to see him? You could pretend you're thinking of having a nose job,' she suggested.

My hands flew to my face. 'Do you think I need a nose job?' I asked.

She rolled her eyes. 'Of course not, but it would be an excuse to see him, then you could go in and act all surprised that you've bumped into your ex.'

I got up and fetched a notebook so I could make a list of possible plans. 'Or,' she continued, 'you could fake a medical event, like a conference or a ball, and invite him to turn up to that, only when he arrives it's just you there.'

'I'd look like a stalker,' I exclaimed. 'There's no way I'm doing that. He'd think I was nuts.'

'You could ring him and say that you just realised that you were near his office and did he fancy a coffee for old times' sake?' she suggested.

'That's a pretty good idea,' I said, and Charmaine sat

70

back looking triumphant. 'But how will I explain how I knew where his office was without admitting that I looked him up, and looking like a psycho ex again?'

She pouted and sat for a moment, thinking. 'You could pretend you're writing a book and you need to do some background research? You could say you're writing to doctors that you knew so you can interview them?'

'What if he wants to see a copy of my book when it's written?' I asked.

'Loads of writers get ideas that don't pan out. Besides, once you've met with him, you don't need to contact him again, just say whatever you need to get him to meet you.'

I wasn't sure, but it was the best plan that we'd come up with so I picked up my mobile and rang the number listed on the screen before I could chicken out.

Chapter Twelve

It turned out that all our plotting was unnecessary. As soon as Rob came on the line he was surprised but not displeased to hear from me, and had suggested that we go out for a coffee. We agreed to meet at the British Museum the following Saturday, and hung up without me needing to explain why I had rung him in the first place.

I chose my outfit for the meeting carefully, wanting to look both cute but professional, in case I did need to fall back on my pretence of interviewing him for a book. I finally settled on a navy blue and white cotton sundress, which ended just above my knees and went perfectly with some little blue kitten heels. I brushed my hair and left it hanging loose over my shoulders. Rob had loved running his hands through it when we'd dated.

I picked up my handbag and put in a notebook and pen, just in case, then walked up to the train station to head into town.

The British Museum never failed to take my breath away. The magnificent atrium with its sweeping staircases and high roof left me with a sense of awe. I glanced at my watch and realised that I still had ten minutes before I was due to meet Rob, so I walked around the grand entrance admiring the sense of space.

I still had a couple of minutes to spare, when I felt a hand on my elbow. I jumped, and turned to see Rob. His pale blue eyes twinkled as he greeted me and I wondered why he had agreed to come, though I was glad he did. He'd left the white coat and stethoscope at home, and yet he still retained the aura of calmness and confidence that I associated with doctors. Perhaps they needed those attributes, as they were responsible for making life and death judgements. Whatever it was, I was jealous because I felt as jumpy as hell.

'Shall we wander round as we talk?' Rob suggested. 'No matter how many times I visit, I never get tired of admiring the exhibits here.'

I followed him round as he led the way, pointing out some of his favourite pieces and giving me a history lesson as he went. By the time we got to the coffee shop, my feet were aching, and my head felt fuzzy from trying to take it all in. I bought us drinks, but left Rob to carry the laden tray to a table. My hands weren't steady enough and I was nervous of spills, but he was a surgeon so shouldn't have the same problem.

'So what did you really want to talk to me about?' he asked as he handed me my hot chocolate. 'Not that it hasn't been lovely to see you again.'

I stopped to consider whether I wanted to go with my excuse of interviewing him, but as he sat and looked me in the eye, I decided that I would go with the truth.

'I've been reminiscing recently, and I realised that I hadn't been very fair to you when we went out,' I said.

'What do you mean?' he asked.

I'd never told him before about sleeping with George, and I didn't plan to now, but somehow he had guessed that when I came back after my weekend at home something had changed. 'I should never have let one fight get in the way of us having a chance, I guess,' I told him.

'I kicked myself for ages when I thought about how rude I was to you,' he admitted. 'And that I sulked for so long and didn't apologise.'

'I never meant to mess you around,' I said, my cheeks blushing as I said it.

'It wasn't your fault alone that we split,' he pointed out,

and I thought that he was being very generous. Even now, years later, I wasn't proud of my behaviour. 'I said lots of things I regretted afterwards,' he continued.

'That level of intimacy was new to me and I don't think I handled it well,' I fudged.

'I did wonder,' he admitted, 'but I didn't exactly manage it better myself, did I?'.

'Well, you met Krista just a few weeks later, so it was a moot point after that anyway. Whatever happened to her? You were together for ages, weren't you? I used to see you on campus now and then looking pretty cosy.' I smiled as I said it so that he'd know I wasn't feeling jealous.

'We dated for a couple of years,' he said, sipping his coffee. 'I was starting to think about proposing, but then we ended up with placements at different hospitals and hardly saw each other. I forgot dates that we'd arranged because I stayed late with patients who needed my help. Krista said I made her feel like she came last in my long list of priorities, but then she refused to understand how important my career is to me. Perhaps I hadn't changed as much as I thought I had. I didn't apologise to her much either.' He gave a smile but it was wistful.

'So are you seeing anyone now?' I asked, and then wondered why I had.

He set his cup down slowly and looked up at me. 'I'm not, but I'm afraid I don't think us getting back together would be a good idea.'

I laughed quickly, and a look of hurt flashed across his face. 'I'm sorry,' I said, reaching out and gently touching his hand for a moment. 'That wasn't what I meant. I didn't mean to give you the wrong idea by getting in touch again after all this time. I've had a couple of lucky escapes recently that got me thinking about my past and reminiscing, that's all. I've always felt guilty about how

I treated you, and I wanted to know if you were happy, that's all.'

'I am,' he assured me. 'You didn't put me off dating, so please let your mind be set at ease. Come on, the weather outside is gorgeous, let's walk for a while.'

I followed him out and he led us through Russell Square and up towards Tottenham Court Road and the enormous superstores of the West End.

Having clarified that I wasn't there to try and initiate a new relationship with him he opened up and told me a little more about his personal life. 'I was never sure what specialty I wanted to go into,' he said as we walked, 'but my dad invited me to join his practice and I've had some wonderful experiences. His colleagues are quick to let me watch their surgeries and scrub in on cases I'd never get to see otherwise.'

'So it isn't all desperate housewives needing boob jobs?' I asked.

He grinned and shook his head. 'Not my area of expertise,' he said, and we both went quiet. I wondered if he was thinking about how he'd fumbled with my bra the first time I let him try and remove it. He coughed, and continued with his explanation. 'I concentrate on facial work at the moment. There's some elective work, of course, but also a lot of repairs needed after illnesses or accidents, and it's incredibly rewarding to see how much I can help rebuild someone's self-esteem when it goes well.'

I wondered when he mentioned self-esteem if he could tell just from our brief time together that day that mine was lower than it had been when I had last seen him.

'I'm an English teacher now,' I told him. 'But I work in East London and I'm never quite sure how much I'm actually helping people.'

He laughed. 'I'm sure your students appreciate you,' he

said, and I didn't tell him about the caricature I'd found on the floor after a lesson once that made me out to look like a carrot with a face on it.

'But to answer your question from earlier,' he continued, 'I am single currently, but I don't mind. I date when I want to, but I'm working fairly long hours and it suits me not to have to worry about having to fit work around anyone else. Once I finish this programme next year I might start to think again, but for now this lifestyle suits me.'

We found a small park just off the main road and, though every square inch of grass was covered by people sunbathing and making the most of the odd few warm days, there was a space on a bench and we sat down.

'And you? I take it you're single then too?' Rob asked me.

'I am,' I confirmed. 'And I've decided to stay that way until I work out where I've been going wrong.'

'And have I helped you with your research?' he asked, spreading his arms across the back of the bench and raising his face to bask in the sun for a moment.

'You have,' I assured him, thinking about how I'd learnt to try and slow down and not rush head first into stupid choices, to face my problems and not run from them. Facing up to Rob had been far easier than I had dared to hope for after all. 'For what it's worth, I am sorry I messed up. I didn't mean to hurt you.'

'I was never cross with you,' Rob assured me. 'Not really. I was angry with myself for being young and full of hormones. For what it's worth, I have tried since then to be a little more understanding and patient with my partners.'

Realising that Rob had needed the time and space for his own career was reassuring. As was finally letting go of the guilt that I'd messed up what could have been a good relationship by sleeping with George instead. Even if we hadn't broken up when we had, we surely would have before long under the pressure of study demands, or possibly just the natural course of finding out who we were and what we wanted from life. And wasn't that what university was about, after all.

'It's been nice to see you again,' I told him, and he sat up straight to look at me.

'It's been nice to see you too,' he said. I leant forward and kissed his cheek. Neither of us felt the need to swap telephone numbers.

'Have a happy life,' I told him, as I got up and walked away.

Chapter Thirteen

I wanted to have a happy life, which was partly why I'd
started on this hare-brained scheme in the first place. I
wandered in and out of a few shops on my way to the
station, and thought about my life in general. My flat made
me happy. In truth it was little more than a bedsit, but I'd
rented it at a time when I really needed my own space, and
it suited me perfectly. It represented the independence and
freedom that I'd so desperately needed after I broke up
with Ryan. It was only round the corner from my parents,
but I got on well with them and really enjoyed having
them nearby, or I would, when they returned from holiday
in time for George's wedding. Matt used to whine about
them interfering but it had never bothered me. Maybe
they trusted me not to get into trouble and didn't boss
me around in the same way. Maybe I'd just been better
at hiding my more salacious activities from them. Either
way, now that we were adults they had embraced their
retirement and were on their second trip of the year to
Spain already.

Charmaine was definitely a positive factor in my life,
even if standing next to her made me feel short and very
plain. She had a zest for life that was contagious. I guess
she needed that kind of energy for the late nights and
running around that came with working in a professional
kitchen. She didn't seem to get as easily thrown by life's up
and downs as I did, and yet she was always patient and
understanding with me. For a while – and then she'd drag
me out shopping or to see a band, so that my pity parties
never lasted too long.

Even Matt, who for a long time had teased me until

I wanted to scream, had calmed down in recent years. I wouldn't say that we were best friends, but we could now be in the same room for a few hours without a world war breaking out, and that felt like a great start.

My tutor group would be leaving the school once we reached the summer holidays, and there were one or two kids that I would genuinely miss, though there were enough that I wouldn't so I didn't feel too sad. The head teacher had offered me the opportunity to lead on the English programme for the year sevens when school started again in September, but I'd been too nervous to accept. Whilst it would have looked great on my CV, and would undoubtedly have helped when it was time to move on to another school later, I'd turned it down. I didn't want to take on more responsibility and run the risk of not doing a good enough job. So now I had five glorious empty weeks waiting for me to fill them with books, and walks and sunshine. I planned to sleep until lunchtime on my first day off, just because I could, but then to get up every day and do something exciting and different, just because I could. No one to tell me not to, or to call me lazy or tell me that I wasn't enough, in some way.

Even Bea and Alice made me happy. The little girl was so affectionate it was impossible not to fall in love with her. Despite Bea's recent heartbreak, she had a calmness about her that told me she was going to be okay. I'd promised them after the Dublin trip that I'd visit again, and I resolved to do so once my holidays started.

Which brought me at last to Jake. Even thinking of him made me smile, and I remembered how it felt when he'd kissed me. I found myself wishing that I hadn't pulled back when I'd been dancing with him at the club. I'd pressed just close enough once to get a feel of his muscular frame underneath his shirt, before I'd moved away. He made me laugh, and it was so easy to spend time with him. But I reminded myself of how wrong I'd been about men in the past, and tried to distract myself from thinking about him any more.

I ran my finger along the rack of T-shirts in the shop, stopping when I came across a rich rusty orange one. I held it up against me, and decided to treat myself whilst I was out. They had a stack of fashion magazines by the till, and I picked one up to read in the bath later. A long hot bubble bath would be just what my feet needed after so much walking today.

The tube was busy and I didn't get a seat until I was three stops from home, but I took it gratefully just the same. A five-minute walk at the other end brought me to my front door. It was almost teatime, and the heat of the day had slowly faded, leaving just a warm, hazy evening. It was enough to make me wish that I had a garden so that I could fix a salad for tea and eat outside.

I stood on my doorstep for a moment longer than I needed to, just to catch the last few rays of sunshine before I went inside. I swear sometimes I feel like I'm solar powered, I can almost feel my mood lifting as I warm up, and despite being tired I wasn't ready to be indoors yet.

If I stood there any longer though I'd look like a burglar trying to break in, or like a dizzy woman who had forgotten her keys, so reluctantly I opened the door and started to look forward to sitting down instead, when I heard my name being called. I turned to see Jake and Alice, riding up the street. Well, Alice was propelling herself forward on a little bike that didn't seem to have any pedals, and Jake was jogging alongside, bent over to stay at the same height as her, trying to keep up.

Alice was giggling, and having a great time. Jake looked slightly winded, and as he stood up he groaned and stretched out his back. I heard it cracking into place. 'I think you need a soak in the bath more than I do,' I said, walking over and giving Alice a kiss on the top of her head.

'Do I get one of those too?' Jake asked, so I kissed the top of his head as well. Alice giggled.

'My daddy got me a bike for my birthday,' she told me.

'I didn't know it was your birthday, sweetie,' I said to her, looking up at Jake.

'Sorry,' he said. 'I should have told you.'

'I'm four now,' Alice said, lifting her hand and showing me three fingers.

'If it's okay with your mummy maybe I can come over one day soon and we can celebrate,' I said.

'We've got cake,' Alice said.

'I wasn't allowed to help bake it,' Jake added.

Alice began to pedal off down the road, and Jake chased after her, calling over his shoulder that he would see me soon. I opened my door, feeling more cheerful for having watched the loving interaction between Jake and his niece. I was bending down to pick up some post when I heard a crash. The sounds of metal crumpling like an empty tin can, and glass shattering held me momentarily frozen, before I dropped the envelopes and ran to the road.

I breathed a sigh of relief when I saw Alice still sat on her little bike, though she was in the gutter by the road, but my stomach flipped when I realised that I couldn't see Jake next to her. I picked Alice up and she complained that I had lifted her from her beloved wheels. I reached down and picked the bike up too, carrying them into the middle of the road with me to find Jake.

The car, a black Volvo, was pulled up, it's front end at ninety degrees facing the kerb opposite. The fender nearest me was folded into a concertina, and the shattered glass of the headlight was scattered across the asphalt. The driver opened his door and got out without pausing to switch off the engine. He dashed around the bonnet, and we both saw Jake lying on the ground, his arm stretched out at an odd angle. There was blood over his face, and I could see dark stains on the road, which I assumed were probably from him too.

Alice started screaming, and I was torn between looking after her and trying to see if I could help Jake. Alice started twisting and wailing in my arms and I tried to hush her. I could hear someone talking loudly on a mobile and realised that the driver was requesting an ambulance. I turned back to Jake, to see the driver drop to one knee next to him and put his ear close to Jake's face.

'He's breathing,' he said into the phone, 'but he's not conscious.'

With Alice still squirming, I stepped closer and knelt next to him but I didn't know what to do. I wasn't sure whether I was supposed to move him into the recovery position, especially given how twisted his arm was. The driver, who must have been in his early forties but had aged ten years just in the last few seconds, seemed as disturbed as I felt. He had just a scattering of sandy coloured hair left on his head, but he was in danger of losing that too if he didn't stop running his hands through it and tugging on it.

He looked up at me and said, 'I didn't see him, he came diving in front of the car.' He shrugged his shoulders and shook his head to try to express his shock at hitting another human body. He was wearing sunglasses, and he pushed them up so they rested on his bald forehead. His grey eyes held mine, and I could see him blink back tears.

I wanted to reassure him, but I couldn't find any words. A siren shattered the quiet, and Alice started to sob again.

I carried her back to the safety of the pavement and held her against me, both of us crying, as the ambulance pulled to a stop next to Jake. The paramedics got out and began to work on him. Within minutes a police car had parked behind the Volvo and the driver was sat inside.

The next few minutes passed in a blur. I was vaguely aware of telling the police that I'd heard the crash but not seen what had happened. They took my contact details and left me to look after Alice. The driver was subjected to a more intense discussion. Even in my distracted state I noticed him being breathalysed. I doubted that he'd be over the limit though, he'd seemed stone cold sober to me on the road, just shaken as hell, and I couldn't blame him for that. I was too.

The paramedics lifted Jake onto a stretcher and carried him into the ambulance. Alice stretched out towards him and started crying again. I held her close and walked towards the vehicle, but the paramedic stopped me with his hand. 'Sorry, love, we need the room to work on him, and if you don't mind me saying, I'm not sure she needs to see that.' He gestured at Alice who was by now sobbing so hard her eyes and nose streamed.

'Which hospital are you taking him to?' I asked.

'We'll be at the General within about five minutes with the blue lights going so you look after your little one and we'll see you there. Try not to worry,' he said, turning his back to us, slamming the door and speeding off in a haze of noise, lights and exhaust fumes.

The police officer took my telephone number and told me that I was free to take Alice home. I didn't have keys to her house, so I took her to mine. I rang Bea, but Alice was crying in the background and I could hear Bea getting more and more distressed as I spoke. I picked up the remote control and flicked through the channels until

I found a TV programme with some brightly coloured puppets flinging slime at each other. I didn't recognise them but Alice immediately calmed down, and so did Bea once she could hear that her little girl was okay.

'Are you all right to watch Alice for a few hours?' she asked me.

I assured her that I was, and she promised to ring me from the hospital when she had any news. Alice was engrossed in the programme, so I took a few minutes to try and calm myself down. My pulse had almost returned to a normal rate, and my hands had stopped shaking, when Alice called out to tell me that she was hungry.

My fridge was almost empty, but I had some flatbreads in the cupboard, some pasta sauce and some cheese, so we stood side by side at the table making our pizzas and choosing toppings. I had sweetcorn and mushroom. Alice had raisins and carrots. I wasn't sure how that would work out, but she was adamant, as only a small child can be, and as it distracted her from thinking about Jake, I let her try it. She could always pick them off later if she didn't like it, or eat mine. I wasn't sure I could stomach any food until I heard how Jake was.

I kept checking my mobile, but by seven o'clock there was still no news from Bea. I rang the hospital but as I wasn't family they couldn't tell me anything. In the background I heard Alice's programme end, and the screen went blue. She looked at me with her big blue eyes, and yawned. Despite the churning in my stomach, I tried to hide it to keep her as calm as I could. She was covered in pizza sauce, and there was a greasy splodge on her T-shirt where the raisins had fallen off as she ate.

'How about you have your bath here,' I suggested. She shook her head, and her curls flew from side to side. I saw her lips purse, and I knew that I had moments to salvage it before she started weeping again. 'I've got bubbles,' I told her. 'Let's go and make bubble splat pies.' I tried to smile, and it must have looked passable, because she took my hand and came with me.

I ran her a deep, deep bath, and she played happily for half an hour. We took it in turns to pile bubbles in our hands, then clap and see how far we could make the bubbles fly. Alice laughed especially hard when she made them fly all over my once dry clothes.

I got her out, wrapped her up in a towel and realised that I didn't have any clean clothes to put her in. She wanted to put her dirty T-shirt back on, but eventually I realised that if I turned things into a game, she was much more likely to let me do as I needed. It was hard to act cheerful when I couldn't tear my mind away from worrying about Jake, but thankfully Alice seemed unaware of all the drama and I knew she needed me to look after her so I tried to concentrate on what I could usefully do. I put one of my T-shirts on my bed and told her I hoped no one put it on. She giggled as I turned my back, and when I turned back again she was wearing it and laughing at me. It came down to her ankles, but at least it was clean.

Likewise, I got her a fresh toothbrush out of the cupboard and she let me brush her teeth as I pretended to be looking to see if she'd hidden her pizza in her cheeks. I tucked her into my bed and remembered that despite being an English teacher, the only books in my flat were those suitable for older children and adults, so I made up a story about a superhero called Alice, who could fly and never had to eat her broccoli, and eventually after three renditions of 'Twinkle Twinkle Little Star', Alice fell asleep.

There were still no messages on my mobile, and by now I was getting frantic, so I phoned the hospital again. Still they were unable to tell me anything. The panic bubbled away in the pit of my stomach until I felt sick.

I wanted a glass of wine, but given that I was looking after Alice I decided that I'd better stick to tea. Even avoiding caffeine and choosing camomile didn't really help to settle my nerves. I picked up my phone and was about to ring Bea again when there was a knock at my door.

Chapter Fourteen

I let Bea in and got her settled on the sofa. Her usually immaculate hair was pulled back into a scruffy bun, and she had bags under her eyes. I walked into the kitchen and fetched her a glass of wine. She took a long drink, then sighed.

'Thanks, Evie, I needed that,' she said. 'And thanks for watching Alice.'

'She was as good as gold,' I assured her, then stood up and waved her to come and peep into my bedroom. Alice was fast asleep in my bed clutching my old teddy bear. Bea looked like she needed to join her.

We walked back to the living room and Bea dropped back onto the sofa. 'Do you mind if Alice stays a bit longer?' she asked.

'Of course not,' I replied. 'How is Jake doing?'

Bea rubbed her face with her hands. She took a deep breath and I saw her shoulders relax and drop from their hunched position up by her neck. Perhaps she could think about him again now that she knew that Alice was okay. 'He had a dislocated shoulder, which they've re-set, and he has a broken wrist they had to pin. He is going to be in plaster for the next six weeks. He also got knocked out, so he has to stay in overnight because he had lost consciousness at the scene, but the doctor assured me that head injuries often bleed a lot and look worse than they in fact are, so I'm hoping that he'll be home again tomorrow.'

'If there is anything I can do to help, please just let me know,' I told her, and she nodded her head.

'I'm afraid I'll have to,' she said. 'Jake needs his pyjamas and a washbag. I told him I'd go home and get them.' She motioned to a bag at her feet. 'I wanted to go back and take these to him, but I had to see Alice first. I knew she was fine here with you, but after the shock of seeing Jake covered in blood, I just had to see my baby too.'

'Have you eaten?' I asked her. She shook her head. I walked back into the kitchen, found the pizza that I hadn't been able to manage and set it to warm up. 'You stay here,' I told her. 'The food will be ready in five minutes. I'll put another fresh T-shirt out for you, and you can sleep next to Alice. I'll take the clothes to Jake and when I get back I can sleep on the sofa.'

'I can't ask you to do that,' Bea said, but she yawned as she said it and looked longingly in the direction of my bedroom.

'You're not asking, I'm offering, and you need to rest. Alice will need you tomorrow, and so will Jake by the sounds of things.' I grabbed my jacket and car keys. 'Help yourself to anything you need. Alice used the new pink toothbrush in the bathroom, and there are clean towels in the cupboard.'

It was late evening by the time I pulled into the car park and I had my choice of spaces. I guess I'd missed visiting hours and hoped that they would let me in to see Jake. I followed the directions Bea had given me and found his ward up three flights of stairs and down several long corridors. The doors to the ward were closed, so I knocked. A nurse opened them and pointed to a board that displayed the times when they accepted visitors, but I held up my bag and told her I was only there to drop something off. I breathed a huge sigh of relief when she let me in.

Jake was sat up in bed, fiddling with a television mounted onto a thin metal stand. It had a phone on one side, and looked like a space age communication unit. I handed him his bag and leaned over and kissed his cheek. His stubble grazed my lips, and up close I could see how pale he was. I pulled him against me for a proper hug, and he winced as I accidentally brushed his injured shoulder.

'I'm sorry,' I said, pulling away.

He held onto my hand. 'Nothing to be sorry for,' he said.

'What happened?' I asked him, taking back my hand and sitting on the chair next to his bed. I hoped he couldn't tell how much I'd wanted to keep hold of his hand. 'I was just closing my door and I heard the crash but I didn't see anything.'

'It's a bit fuzzy,' he told me. 'It all happened so fast, but as far as I can remember, Alice was sat on the kerb on her little bike. We were waiting for the car to pass, but it was going really slowly as it neared the speed bump, which was lucky for me as it turned out.'

I looked at the cast on his arm and the thin lines of red dots of blood marking the graze on his forehead where he had hit the ground. I thought about how bad it could have been had the car been travelling any faster and found myself feeling sick.

'I messed up though and we were waiting by a dip in the kerb. I thought that would make it easier for Alice to cross, but she started to roll forward into the road just as the car got close to us, so I dived in front, pushed her back to the kerb, but got knocked flat on my backside for my troubles. I broke my wrist and dislocated my shoulder as I fell, then cracked my head on the road for good measure.'

'I'm just relieved that you're okay,' I told him.

'I have to stay in overnight in case of concussion,' he told me, 'but I don't feel too bad right now. That may change when the painkillers they gave me wear off.'

I handed him the bag. 'I've got your pyjamas,' I said, but he pointed to the cast on his arm.

'I'm not entirely sure how to put them on,' he said.

I sat on the side of his bed, trying to weigh up whether I should offer to help him or not. I didn't like to leave him to struggle, but the thought of taking off his hospital gown and re-dressing him felt so intimate. I imagined his bare chest, and how it would feel to slip the pyjama bottoms over his legs. I felt myself blush, and his smile grew wider. 'I'm sure I'll manage,' he said, and I was surprised to find that I felt disappointed. 'Unless you wanted to help?'

I shook my head and got up to go. 'Please wait,' Jake said, touching my hand again. 'Just wait outside the curtain for a minute, please.'

I nodded, not trusting myself to speak. I was so relieved to see for myself that he was okay. I pulled the curtain around his cubicle to give him the privacy to change and listened to the swishing of fabric. I heard him puffing with the effort. He fell silent for a minute, and then I heard his voice, softly calling my name. I peeked back round the curtain to find him sat on his bed. He'd managed to get his pyjama bottoms up to his knees, I helped him stand and I pulled them up to cover his boxer shorts. He held on to my shoulders to steady himself.

'Thank you,' he said. 'I thought I could manage but as I bent over to pull them on I felt dizzy. Maybe it is lucky that I'm in here after all.'

I smiled and tied the drawstring at his waist. I slipped the hospital gown over his head and helped him get the pyjama top over his cast. He tried to do the buttons himself but I watched him wince as he used his left hand and stepped in front of him. He didn't speak as I fastened the buttons, and when I finished I found that I couldn't step away. Instead I brushed the hair from his eyes and placed a gentle kiss on his forehead.

He reached out and put his uninjured arm around my

waist, pulling me closer against him. I tried to blink the tears from my eyes but I couldn't stop them from falling. 'I was so scared,' I told him.

He buried his head against my stomach, and I stroked his hair, gently to avoid brushing against his injuries again, as my tears fell silently.

'I'm okay,' he reassured me. 'A bit bruised but nothing that won't heal.'

'You were a hero,' I told him, as I sniffed and tried to pull myself together.

'Hardly,' he said with a small snort. 'I was the plonker who nearly let Alice roll into the road in front of a car.'

'You were the one who risked your own life to pull her out of the way. Accidents happen,' I told him, 'but you stopped this one from being a damn sight worse.'

'How is Alice?' he asked.

'She's fine,' I reassured him. 'Not a scratch on her. I left her fast asleep in my flat, and Bea not far behind. I told Bea that I'd bring you the bag so she could rest, she looked done in, but the truth was I needed to see for myself that you were all right.'

Jake looked so vulnerable, sat on his hospital bed with the plaster cast immobilising his wrist. The dim lights of the corridor, made even more subdued by the curtains still pulled shut around us, left his face in shadow. His arm, still around my waist stretched up to stroke the back of my neck. I bent down so that he could reach me more easily, and he guided me down further, until he could reach me with his lips.

His kiss was tender and sweet. I returned it with a hunger that left me breathless. Jake leant back on his bed and I climbed on top, straddling him without breaking contact with our lips. He winced when his shoulder touched the bed, I started to pull back but he held onto me with his good arm and brought me down against him. Everything that had held us back before no longer seemed important. The only thing that mattered was that Jake was still alive and we were together.

I kissed his throat and started to unbutton the top I'd only just done up for him. My heart was beating so hard he could probably hear it. He groaned and this time I did stop. I climbed off him and stood next to the bed.

'I'm sorry,' I said. 'I didn't mean to hurt you.' I wanted to look at him but I couldn't bring myself to meet his eyes.

He took my hand. 'You didn't,' he assured me. 'We don't need to stop. Hell, I'd risk breaking my other arm to kiss you again.'

I reached down and picked up my handbag. 'I'd better go,' I told him. 'You need to rest.'

'I'll see you soon,' Jake told me. 'You can come and visit me and sign my cast.' I nodded but still didn't look at him. 'Evie, it's okay,' he said. I glanced at him and saw that there was a ghost of a smile on his face.

I nodded at him again, and left.

Chapter Fifteen

I was tired to my bones when I got home, but even as I fetched a pillow and blanket and made myself a nest, I knew I would hardly sleep. It had nothing to do with being on the sofa instead of in my bed. More, it was because every time I closed my eyes I had images of Jake: the first time I saw him, surrounded by the chaos of his attempt at cooking, he'd been the calm in the eye of a storm, and utterly gorgeous; and then as he looked when I left him, injured, but peaceful, and still breathtakingly beautiful.

I thought about how it had felt to kiss him. The kiss we'd shared in Dublin had been playful, teasing almost. He had claimed to be helping me out in my mission. I put yesterday's kiss down to me reassuring myself that he was really all right after the scare. I tried not to think about how good it had felt to be pressed against him, or how much he had seemed to be enjoying it too. I needed to be more careful around him, maybe try and give myself a bit more space until I had completed my mission and worked out for myself where I'd been going wrong in my relationships. Jake was amazing, so caring and thoughtful. I didn't know whether he had any feelings for me and, if he did, whether he was ready to explore them now that the shock of the accident had passed but I didn't want to risk messing up again if it had signified more.

I reached under the sofa and drew out my notebook. After Rob I'd had a bit of a dry spell. I had been so angry with myself that for six months I hadn't gone near another man. Eventually though, I'd folded. My mum had no idea why I had been a bit flat, but she had clearly decided to do something about it. She told Matt that he was taking me with him when he went out, and so he did, but under protest and so I spent the evening nursing a pint whilst he flirted shamelessly with any girl who looked at him twice.

Eventually Matt found someone willing to take him home. He asked George to make sure I got back safely, and off he went. I'd told George that I'd be perfectly safe walking by myself, but he pointed out that Matt would be pissed off if he didn't do what he had been asked. I found myself tussling over the emotions inside. I was still attracted to George, why wouldn't I be? He was six foot of testosterone. Black hair and eyes the colour of chocolate with a washboard stomach from playing so much sport. I wasn't sure who would protect me from being with him. I didn't think I would be able to stop myself.

I was angry with myself for using him last time and, despite his reputation with women, it had very much been me leading the way when I'd slept with him. But in a funny way, I also cared about him. He'd been so tender, and he hadn't pushed me into anything, in fact, quite the opposite, he'd been almost surprised that I'd wanted to and had asked me if I was sure so many times in the end I'd told him to stop talking and start doing it already. The lack of conversation afterwards may not have been ideal, but I'd been more than a willing partner.

So as we walked, I wasn't surprised when he reached for my hand. We hadn't talked since, and I'd deliberately not spent as much time at home, but, as always, once you've broken through a barrier it is harder to go back. As we reached the corner of my road he pulled me against him and kissed me.

'The first time isn't always that much fun,' he told me.

'You're telling me,' I said. 'You were very gentle, but, yeah, it was a bit sore the next day.'

'I'm sorry,' he said, letting his hands glide over my backside.

'It's okay,' I reassured him. 'And it wasn't your fault. You were very sweet to me.'

'Has it been better for you since then?' he asked.

I took a deep breath and wondered what to tell him, but there was no point lying. He was a close enough friend that I wanted to tell him the truth, plus I knew he would never tell anyone. He'd never be able too because Matt would have killed him.

'I haven't slept with anyone else,' I said.

'Let me show you how much better it can be.'

I nodded, and led him to my house and upstairs to my bed. He was right, the second time was better. I was more relaxed, and it didn't sting this time. It wasn't earth moving good, but it was fun. Afterwards George got up and started to get dressed.

'Why did you come back with me?' I asked him as he reached for his pants.

'I wanted you to know how good sex can feel,' he said, pulling his T-shirt back over his head.

'But why show me?' I asked, watching him.

'You seemed upset, I wanted to cheer you up.' As if everyone used sex where a hug might have sufficed.

'Matt would be furious if he knew,' I said, reaching for my own nighty.

'I wasn't planning to tell him,' George said with a grin, 'and I'd appreciate it if you didn't either.'

'No fear,' I said. 'I don't want to see him kill you any more than you do. But knowing how much it would piss him off, why did you sleep with me?' I knew I shouldn't ask. The answer might well be as simple as that I was female and willing. I was certain that it wouldn't be any declarations of undying love.

'These things happen sometimes,' he said. It was a cop out answer. It had happened because we had made it happen.

'Why do you do it, knowing how much it would upset your brother?' he asked me, sitting back on my bed and holding his trousers in his hand.

That question made me pause for a while as I tried to think how best to answer. 'I wouldn't want to upset Matt,' I told him, 'but equally the fear of that isn't strong enough to stop me. I wanted to do something just for myself. I see him do that all the time. And I feel safe with you. We've known each other long enough.'

'I won't hurt you,' George said, looking me in the eye, 'but I also won't make any promises I can't keep. This is what it is.'

'I figured that out,' I assured him. 'And I'm old enough to know what I'm doing.'

'You're very pretty,' he said, tucking a strand of hair behind my ear.

'I'm not,' I replied. 'You've seen Charmaine. I don't have the legs or the boobs.'

'She's eye-catching,' George said, and I knew that if he said any more about her I'd have to kill him myself, 'but don't put yourself down. You should be sure of yourself. You're easy to talk to. I like how you listen to me. Some guys really dig the quiet ones too, you know.'

'Do you?' I asked, then realised that I was straying dangerously close to the line of what it was okay to expect of him.

'Sometimes,' he said, grinning at me. 'I like a lot of different types of women.' That was an understatement. I suspected that Matt and George had very few types of women they didn't like. 'But you know what I find most attractive of all in women?' he asked me.

I shook my head, wondering whether he'd be offended if I'd answered with my first response of a vagina and a pulse.

'Confidence,' he said. 'Seeing women who know what they want and aren't afraid to get it.'

I snorted and he continued. 'I don't just mean in bed, though I'd be lying if I said that I turn down women who know what they want and who come on to me to get it. I just mean that you're a bright girl, you're cute, don't hide it away. If you want people to notice you, you have to show them that you have something worth noticing.'

I'd gone back to college with a renewed sense of confidence after that little pep talk. George may not have wanted to commit to me, but he always left me feeling as though I was worthy of someone else's attention. Perhaps that was why I was always drawn back to him.

I finished reading the page and tucked the notebook back under the sofa just as Alice came bursting in to the room. She jumped up beside me, squashing my legs. I groaned and reached up to tickle her.

'Let Evie wake up gently,' Bea called from the doorway.

'It's okay, I'm up,' I assured her. 'I'll make us some coffee,' I said, getting up.

Chapter Sixteen

Four more days and I would be on summer break. It was so close now that I was starting to find it as hard to concentrate as my students did. My thoughts drifted back to the weekend. Jake had been released on the Sunday and Bea had picked him up and taken him home to recover. I'd babysat Alice and had dashed away as soon as they'd returned. I'd claimed that Jake had needed to rest, but the truth was I wasn't sure what to say to him about the kiss.

I spent a fraught hour trying to get my year nine group to understand the subtext of *Animal Farm*. I thought it was finally sinking in, until one lad asked me why if the animals could talk they hadn't simply gone on TV. I tried to hide my groan but I think they were as relieved as I was when the bell rang.

I spent another hour trying to talk to my year sevens about the difference between nouns, verbs and adverbs. By the end of the session I think one kid had got it, several were so bored that they'd had a long debate about the merits of various contestants on the *X Factor*, despite my best attempts to keep them interested, and I was no longer sure I knew or cared what the terms meant either.

I should have stayed after school and tidied the classroom. Thankfully this close to the holidays I didn't have the usual weight of marking and planning to do, so I felt less guilty about ducking out at four o'clock and walking home. Once back in my flat, I treated myself to a long soak in a bubble bath. Despite being so close to the holidays, it still felt odd to wear pyjamas before dinner, so instead I found a little deep green cotton summer dress that floated around my knees, and put that on.

I had my head stuck in the freezer trying to think what I should have for dinner when my mobile rang. The caller display said that it was Bea, so I answered, only to nearly drop the phone when Jake's voice greeted me instead.

'Sorry, did I make you jump?' he asked. He must have heard the sharp intake of breath I had taken. 'We're having a takeaway and wondered if you wanted to join us. We're all too tired to cook and I guessed you might be too.'

'That's really kind,' I said, 'but you need to take it easy, not have a house full of people.'

'You're hardly a house full,' he responded. 'Come on, I hear the Full Moon does a decent tofu dish.'

I stared at my choices of oven chips or something I could no longer identify in a Tupperware box half buried in ice.

'Do you want me to pick it up on my way over?' I offered.

'I called the order in twenty minutes ago,' he said. 'If you come over now it should be here any time.'

I smiled as I hung up, glad that he hadn't called to talk to me about the kiss. Not that I knew what I'd say to him if he did. Walking over to pick up my keys I caught sight of myself in the mirror. My long ginger hair hung down my back, I slicked some lip gloss on and thought about picking up a loose shirt to cover my bare shoulders. Then I thought about what George had told me all those years ago about being proud of myself, being confident and showing myself off, and decided not to. I locked the door behind me and walked over to see my friends.

Bea let me in, and I was relieved to see that her eyes weren't as tired as they often looked. She greeted me with a hug and walked back into the kitchen. A carrier bag was set on the table, and Jake was passing out containers with his good arm. His injured wrist was held tight against his body in a blue sling. He walked over and greeted me with a kiss on the cheek. I think it took about five minutes for my pulse to drop back to normal afterwards.

Alice was dressed in a pink tutu and wellies and was dancing around the kitchen as she sang to herself. I was glad to see Jake up and about, and even more glad to do so in company so that we couldn't talk about the other night.

I spooned some tofu onto my plate and thanked Jake for the noodles that he passed me. Bea was making deals with Alice about how much she had to eat before she could have some prawn crackers. There were footsteps on the stairs and I nearly jumped when a man walked into the kitchen. He was an older version of Jake. They had the same eyes and jawline, though his hair was shorter and mostly white.

'Evie, this is my dad, Pete,' Jake said.

'I can see the resemblance,' I said, standing up and reaching out to shake his hand.

'He wishes to be as handsome as me,' Pete joked. 'I've come to help out for a few days.'

'I couldn't take any more time off,' Bea said. 'I'm going to ring around the local nurseries tomorrow and see if any of them have spaces over the summer for Alice. With her being so happy with Jake, I had thought about waiting until September when she can start at the Acacia School on Old Street, but I'm not sure what I'm going to do until then now that Superman here is out of action. Jake had planned to ask any job that came up now to wait until then for him to start, it's only a few weeks after all, but now I'm nearly as stuck as he is.'

She tousled Jake's hair as she said it, and I could see that she meant it with affection and wasn't cross with him for the change of plans. Especially given that he'd been injured in the line of duty when protecting Alice.

'I keep telling you I'm only down one arm, I can still manage,' he said.

'You can barely wipe your own backside,' his dad said.

'Dad,' Bea exclaimed as Alice started laughing.

She started shouting, 'Grandad said bum bum, Granddad said bum bum,' and Bea shot her dad a look.

'I never had this problem with my childminder.'

'At least I'm not going to chase halfway round the world after my boyfriend and leave you scuppered for childcare with no notice. And I didn't say bum,' he pointed out.

'You just said it,' Alice cried out, and curled up on the floor laughing and holding her sides.

'I can help,' I offered, watching Alice. The giggles were infectious and soon we were all joining in. Bea looked years younger when she smiled.

'Really?' Bea asked. I looked back at her and saw the hope on her face.

'I finish school this week, then I have five weeks off. I can help, until Jake gets the cast off at least,' I said.

Bea walked over and hugged me. I finally looked at Jake. He had a huge grin on his face, and I started to have second thoughts.

Chapter Seventeen

After the meal, I begged off with tiredness and told them that I needed to go. Jake offered to walk me home, but he still looked a little exhausted, so Bea told him to sit down, saying that she fancied some fresh air and that she would walk with me instead. Pete took Alice up to start getting ready for bed, and so when we got back to my flat I invited Bea in for a glass of wine.

She took it and sipped her drink as she sat on the sofa. 'Did something happen with you and Jake the other night?' she asked. 'If he said anything rude he was concussed and I'm sure he didn't mean to,' she said. 'It's just that you hardly looked at him today, and you guys had been getting on so well.'

I sat my glass back on the coffee table. 'He didn't put his foot in it,' I assured her. 'If anything it was me.'

She didn't say anything, just watched me over the rim of her glass. The room fell silent and I found myself talking to fill the space. 'I kissed him,' I admitted.

She set her glass down and grinned. 'I knew it,' she said. 'You do like each other.'

'I feel a bit weird talking about this with his sister,' I admitted.

She waved it away. 'We're adults. I can handle hearing about my brother, especially given that we know you, Evie, and I'm happy for him.'

'Wait, wait,' I said, trying to stop her getting carried away. 'It was just a kiss. I was so relieved to see that he was okay. There were hours where I didn't know how badly hurt he was.'

'So it was a little "glad you're alive" kiss?'

'Not such a little one,' I admitted, blushing as red as my wine. I picked the glass up and tried to hide behind it.

'So are you seeing each other?' she asked.

'I don't know.'

'Do you want to see him?'

I took a mouthful of wine and used the time to put my response together. 'I don't know,' I repeated. I never said it was going to be a useful answer.

'He's a really lovely guy,' I began.

'I think so too, but I am biased,' she said, smiling at me to show that she really was okay discussing her brother in this way.

'I'm just not looking for anything serious right now.'

'Who says it has to be serious?' she asked, grinning at me. 'You can just get to know him, see how it goes. It looks like you're going to be spending a lot of time together over the next few weeks looking after Alice anyway.'

'I know,' I said. 'And I'm looking forward to it. Spending time with Alice, I mean.' I blushed again. 'And with Jake obviously, even if nothing else happens.'

Bea kicked her sandals off and curled up on my sofa. I saw any chances of this being a quick chat go out the window. I stood up and went to fetch ice cream, partly because I thought that matters of the heart should always be discussed over ice cream, and partly to give me more time to pull myself together. I handed Bea a pot of triple flavoured swirl, and admitted to myself that it hadn't worked. I was as mixed up as her dessert. She grew serious as she tucked in. 'Give him time, Evie. I know you're working through your own issues right now, but so is Jake, even if he isn't telling you. He used to look up to my ex like a big brother. I think our divorce was hard on him too. He was pretty quick to turn up when I needed help.'

'How are you holding up? Are you dating again?' I asked her.

She shook her head. 'It's different for me, I have Alice. And I've just been through a divorce. I think that buys me extra time to be by myself.' She gestured at me with her spoon. 'You should go out with Jake.'

'Assuming he even wants to go out with me,' I said as Bea shook her head at me. 'He might not,' I said defensively. Just because he got turned on when I'd climbed all over him at the hospital, it didn't mean that he wanted to date me.

She reached into her pocket and pulled out her phone. Scrolling through, she turned the screen and showed me a picture. It was of a pencil drawing of me, asleep on the plane on the way home from Dublin. Jake had captured the sense of peace I'd gained from spending time with him. There were no grey bags under my eyes any more, or tension lines on my forehead. I looked serene.

'You think someone who doesn't care about you could draw you like that?' Bea asked.

'It's beautiful.' I reached for the phone so that I could see it again. 'Jake's an amazing artist.'

'He's not a bad human being either. Don't run away from this, whatever it turns out to be. That's all I'm asking. I think he's getting ready to open up just as much as you are, in his own way.'

'I won't,' I promised her. Then, as we were being honest, I added 'I don't think you should hide behind Alice forever either. I know you got hurt, but Alice is a great kid. Any guy would be lucky to have the pair of you, and you must get lonely sometimes.'

'I do,' she agreed. 'But I'm in no rush to have my heart stomped on all over again. No, I think I'll hold out until I find someone good enough for me, or maybe I'll just wait until hell freezes over, which might happen first.'

'I'm scared too,' I whispered.

She stopped eating and looked at me. My hands were shaking so I set my glass down before I spilled it.

'What happened to you?' she asked. 'Did someone hurt you too?'

I shook my head. 'It wasn't as dramatic as that, but it did make me stop and think. I think I lost sight of who I was for a while back there, and I needed to do something that helped me to remember.'

'Hence your tracking down old boyfriends,' she said.

'I know it sounds weird, and I must admit there have been a few times that I've felt downright creepy doing it. I was nervous that they'd think I'd been a crazed stalker all these years, but I had to try.'

'And has it helped?' she asked.

'I haven't finished yet,' I pointed out, 'but so far so good. It has been nice to think back to simpler times, when I used to fall for guys just because of how they looked, or how they made me feel and without any regard for whether it could go anywhere. I was remembering being nineteen and someone telling me for the first time that I was pretty and that I should be more confident. That was a nice memory.'

'So who is next on your list?' she asked.

I wondered how much detail it was appropriate to go into. I was fairly sure she wouldn't tell Jake every word I said, but there were some things I wanted to keep to myself. Fresh from my chat with George, I'd tried to act more assertively. I'd gone back to university after the Christmas break and auditioned for the amateur dramatics society.

The society put on a play once a term. I'd expected more of my fellow English Literature students to sign up, especially given how many of us were taking the scriptwriting module that semester, but when I stood on stage, trying to impress the panel with my monologue, I didn't know anyone else in the hall.

I tried to use this to my advantage, as if I embarrassed myself I would never need to see any of these people again, so I took a deep breath and delivered my speech. Although the play I was auditioning for was a dramatic piece, I'd prepared a monologue that Cher delivers in *Witches of Eastwick*, which details why Jack Nicholson's character isn't good enough for her. Given my new-found self-assurance, it seemed appropriate.

I didn't get the role, but I did score a date with the director, Jeremy, or Jem, as he insisted on being called. He was in his twenties and studying for a masters in the performing arts. He wore super skinny black jeans and a leather jacket, and had dyed his hair purple. We dated for six weeks, during which time I saw every open mic night, obscure play and performance art delivered within a hundred miles of our university. We had a whirlwind romance, eating at obscure restaurants, making out in his dingy bedsit.

It had been fun, but slowly the differences crept in. Jem wouldn't hang out with my friends whom he deemed philistines. Eventually I dumped him when he had announced that I was stifling his creative buzz. I made the mistake of inviting him to the cinema to watch a James Bond film. He said that no one who bought into such commercial productions truly valued art.

I told him that no one who sat through the tripe he went to visit knew what art was. We had a fairly dramatic break up, complete with me throwing several mugs at the wall behind him. I wasn't really that angry, I just figured that I'd probably never date anyone with his artistic flair again, and if I wanted to know how it felt to have a proper break up fight, now might be my only chance. Right after I ripped his copy of *Posers Weekly*, or whatever his magazine was really called, and broken down in hysterical laughter, he had stormed out muttering about the crazy redhead and I'd never seen him again.

He had stuck in my memory though, not simply for his clothing choices, but because we'd had a lot of fun together. Not the least of which was that he'd been so inexperienced in bed the first time that I had turned director and told him what I'd wanted him to do. It was worth being assertive with him. Once I'd explained what I needed, he'd been enthusiastic and had been responsible for the first orgasms I'd ever had with another person.

'Just a guy I knew once at uni,' I told Bea, and tried not to blush again at the memories.

Chapter Eighteen

I had expected Jem to either be really easy to find because he'd be a famous director and his name would be buzzing all over the internet, or impossible to find because he'd given up on the developed world and gone to live on the beach in Thailand. Instead, google suggested that Jem Brooks was either a hairdresser in Cardiff or a porn star in Las Vegas. I changed my search term to 'Jeremy Brooks' and got a hit.

There was a PDF of a poster advertising a performance of *A Christmas Carol* in a school three miles away. The poster was a couple of years old, but I googled the school and found a photo of Jem on their website. It was taken side on, showing him pointing at the new school drama facilities. He'd had some success in local theatre, but probably not enough to make a living. I assumed that was why he had trained as a drama teacher. He'd shown no inclination to subsidise his lofty artistic aims in this way when I'd known him.

Back then I had written: *'I met this guy last week. He's not like anyone I've ever met before. He's not as gorgeous as Rob, but he's so interesting. He knows so much about literature and art. He doesn't make me laugh like I do with George, but I feel like I learn something new every time I go out with him.'*

I emailed Charmaine a link to the website, and within a minute had a message back that asked whether I was really sure that I wanted to try and meet up with him again. I wasn't sure what was putting her off, I don't think it was the piercings; goodness knew she'd been out with a few holey guys herself. Maybe it was the fact that despite being almost bald these days, the remains of the ponytail, which he sported, was still dyed purple.

I'd come this far though, and it was important to me to see him. Not just because of the orgasms, though I had enjoyed them, but mostly because I'd known him at the height of my self-confidence, and it was nice to remember how I'd felt. There were only two days remaining of school before the holidays, so I had no time to waste if I didn't want to wait another five weeks to see him.

Normally – if anything about my searches could be considered normal – I'd have tried to ring the school and make up an excuse to meet him, but I decided to be more direct. With exams over for the year, I finished teaching for the day at two o'clock. After straightening up my classroom, I told the school secretary that I had a stonking headache, but instead of driving home, I drove straight over to Jem's school.

Once there, I parked up and walked into the main office. I showed them my school ID card and told their secretary a small white lie. I pretended that I had booked an appointment with Jem to talk to him about his school productions. I kept my fingers crossed that she wouldn't phone him to double check, but luckily the school bell rang for the end of the day, and she was suddenly overwhelmed by the hordes of children streaming around.

She pointed me in the direction of the drama room, and turned back to answer the million and one questions about trips, lunch money and children who had lost their bus fare. I wandered around the corridors, finding the selection of student art and writing decorating the walls reminiscent of every school I'd ever worked in.

The drama department was housed in a separate block, built on to the end of the main corridor. I passed through an archway between the old building and the newer one, and knocked on a door that had been painted black with purple stars. I was in the right place. No one answered my knock, and I hoped I hadn't missed Jem. Tracking him down in the staffroom would make me feel much more like a stalker, though I had my strategy planned. I tried the door and found it unlocked so I walked in. If I couldn't find Jem himself, maybe I could get a sense of who he was now. With Bill Banks and Andy Brown just a brief conversation had been plenty.

I nearly jumped out of my skin when the door opened and Jem was stood right in front of me. He had fine lines now around his eyes, though they were hard to see under his glasses. His jeans were still tight, but not quite the second skin they used to be. Secondary school kids could be brutal, and I wondered whether that was why he now wore a regular black T-shirt and not the floral blouses he used to favour. It was a shame, they had suited him. I wondered how different I looked to him after all these years.

'Hey, ginge,' he said, stepping aside so that I could enter. It was a wonder I hadn't thrown a mug at his head sooner for sticking with that nickname.

'Hey yourself, baldy,' I shot back. Antagonising him wasn't going to help me though, so I swallowed my next insult and stuck my hand out for him to shake. 'This is a surprise,' I lied. 'I work locally and when I contacted your school to ask about their experience of putting on a play with the students they suggested I come and talk to their ama teacher.' I kept my fingers crossed in my pocket as I it, and hoped that he never compared notes and found hat the conversation had never happened.

ncy a coffee?' he asked, stepping back into the room. vanted to avoid chatting with him in public, just we wanted to cover our history and so I was hen he opened another door at the back of the room, which led to a tiny kitchen. He filled the kettle and switched it on. Amazed that he was going to trust me with any crockery, I stayed a few steps behind him in the main room and waited for him. The kitchen was little more than a converted cloakroom, and had I tried to step in too I'd have been as close to him as I used to be, which was certainly not part of my plan.

I looked around as he made the drinks. The room had been painted black, even the windows were painted over, though badly, leaving flakes against the frames and bubbles on the glass. It was impossible to get a sense of time when you couldn't see daylight. The chairs were stacked against the back wall to make for an open performance space, and I could imagine Jem telling the kids to commit to the emotion of the scene. I could also imagine them telling him to piss off. Working in a secondary school could be like that sometimes.

I thought about grabbing a couple of chairs to sit on but it felt too formal to have only two chairs out in an otherwise empty room. There weren't even any posters on the walls. All the better to have a neutral arena. Jem backed out of the kitchen and handed me a mug. 'I don't have a fridge I'm afraid so no milk.'

I thanked him for the coffee and we sat down, back against the wall, legs stretched out in front of us.

'It's nice to see you again, Evie,' he said.

'I'm sorry about breaking your mugs last time,' I replied. 'I promise I'll be careful with this one,' and we both laughed.

'I was a bit precious back then, wasn't I?' Jem remarked.

'And I was making the most of the opportunity to act out,' I replied. We sipped our coffees in silence for a moment. 'This room is great,' I said, trying to build a little rapport again.

'It's a far cry from where I thought I'd end up,' he conceded.

'So what happened?' I asked. 'Not that I think there is anything wrong with where you ended up. I'm a teacher myself too these days.'

'How about we add a drop of the hard stuff to these drinks, really celebrate the holidays in that case,' he suggested. 'I don't know about you but I need some help unwinding after a long day with these little darlings on occasion.'

I nodded and he got up and fetched a bottle of whiskey from the cupboard. 'I keep this to calm me down after watching some of the kids attempt to be particularly dramatic.' He shuddered and I laughed, realising that some things about him really hadn't changed.

He poured a good inch of whiskey into each of our mugs. We clinked and muttered cheers to each other, then sat back in silence for a few moments as we drank. The quiet lasted for so long that I found myself twitching. I gulped the coffee down quicker than I meant to, and the combination of caffeine and alcohol sent my heart racing and made my palms sweaty. I wiped them quickly on my jeans and tried to remember how I'd planned for this conversation to go. I was about to plunge into my explanation again when Jem reached for my empty cup. 'Fancy another?' he asked.

He jumped up before I could answer and headed back out to the cloakroom kitchen. The second mug held more whiskey than coffee, and I knew as I tasted it that I wouldn't be driving again tonight.

'I wanted to ask about school plays,' I began. Jem snorted. 'I did,' I said again. This time he sat back and laughed heartily. 'Why did you make me a drink then? What did you think I was here for?' I asked.

He took the hairband out, shook his hair out and retied it. It didn't look any different and I wondered if he was waiting for me to tell the truth. I wasn't used to daytime drinking any more and found myself blurting out more than I meant to. 'I'm getting in touch with my past, trying to see if I can learn from it. I've been pretty mixed up for a while. I don't want to feel like that any more.'

He'd still barely said a word. He got up and walked back to the kitchen, but this time he made no pretence of making coffee, just grabbed the whiskey and brought it back out.

'So what can I do to help you?' he asked. 'Now that I know that you don't simply want to find out how you can coax a dozen kids who would rather be anywhere near a stage, through a production without wanting to give up and lock yourself in the dressing room whilst you cry.'

Jem topped up our drinks again. If he wasn't careful I'd hardly be able to walk home, let alone order a cab. I wondered how often he needed liquid therapy. He certainly didn't seem to be spinning as much as I was. I set my cup down and tried to sober up.

'Being with you was probably one of the last times I was with someone without questioning my every move,' I said.

He took a deep swallow of his drink. By now it was pure alcohol, no mixer, and I could almost feel the burn for him as it went down. 'What did you worry about after me?' he asked. 'What their taste in movies was doing for your soul?'

I shot him a look and he set his mug down. 'I'm sorry,' he said. 'That was uncalled for. Believe it or not I have actually grown up over the last few years.'

'I know,' I told him. 'There's been something about reliving my past which has made me think again about how I behaved back then, though truthfully it has also been a nice reminder about how it felt to be young and carefree. I guess I always thought that by now I'd have found someone and be settled down, and that I'd understand men and relationships and not be scared by them.'

'What scared you?' Jem asked me. I shook my head and didn't answer him. I hadn't had enough whiskey yet to touch that question. 'I don't think anyone expects you to know all the answers, or to marry the first person you sleep with. Or even the second person.' He looked at me and cocked an eyebrow. 'Or even the third?'

This time I laughed with him. 'I'm not telling. Seriously though,' I said, trying to stop the giggles and realising that I definitely shouldn't drink any more, 'it has been nice to see some of you guys again.'

'And on behalf of your "guys",' he responded with a wink, 'please allow us to say that you have matured well, like a fine wine.' I snorted at that, and hoped that he wasn't about to ask me out again. Turning people down politely when I was drunk had never been my strong suit. He must have sensed my disquiet, as he continued. 'Don't worry, I'm not hitting on you. I don't think Derek would be very pleased with me.'

'Derek?'

He reached into his jeans pocket and pulled out his wallet. Flicking it open, he passed it over and I saw a picture of Jem with his arm around another man. I presumed this was Derek, and I could see why Jem would not want to upset him. Even in the tiny photo he looked heartachingly handsome, with lush lips, a small scar through one eyebrow, and his hair braided in cornrows.

'We got married six months ago,' Jem told me, as I took a huge mouthful of whiskey and promptly ended up coughing half of it back over myself. I didn't speak for a few moments and Jem continued. 'We met at opening night of one of my plays and it was love at first sight. See, I'm married and I still feel like I'm figuring it out one day at a time sometimes.'

He scooted closer to me and put his arm around me, I rested my head on his shoulder.

'He's gorgeous,' I said. 'I'm glad you're happy. Besides, if I wanted to learn about men and relationships, it turns out I came to the right place.'

'Just wondering how I punched above my weight when I met him?' Jem asked, gesturing at the picture again. I grinned, and Jem stood up and held a hand out to help me up. 'Speaking of which, he'll be expecting me home soon.' I took his hand and tried to stand up, at which point I found myself clasping on to him.

'I swear I'm not trying to hit on you either,' I said. 'But would you mind very much holding me up until the room stops spinning?'

Chapter Nineteen

Daylight flooded the room and I sat up, trying to work out where I was. Sadly, the answer was in a world of pain. My head throbbed, and my mouth felt like a cat's litter tray, and not a clean one. I reached for the duvet and pulled it back over my head, ignoring the sense of queasiness in my stomach. I gave up and lay back down again. Clearly I wasn't ready yet to tackle whatever today held.

When I came round again some time later, I no longer felt quite as sick, and the aching in my head had eased a little. I smelt coffee, and emerging from the duvet was handed a mug by the most striking man I've ever seen, and I wasn't just thinking that because he also handed me some painkillers.

'I hear my husband got you drunk last night,' he said. I was about to sit up and try to explain when he laughed, and I swear even that sounded like music, regardless of how delicate my hearing felt.

I took a few mouthfuls of coffee and set it down. Reaching up I found my hair had escaped from my scrunchie overnight and was now sticking up in all directions. I pulled it back into a bun, hoped that I didn't smell like a brewery, and sat back to look at him. Even on my best day I couldn't hold a candle to him, let alone this morning when I was desperately hung-over.

'I'm sorry,' I said. 'I don't usually go round to people's houses and pass out on them.'

'Don't worry,' he said. 'I've been talking to Jem about cutting back on his drinking. I think seeing you get wasted on what he considered a small winding down drink might have helped persuade him that I'm right.'

'Do you have the time please?' I asked as I realised all at the same time that it was both the final day of school before the holiday, and that I was in no fit state to be teaching.

'It's seven o'clock,' Derek told me. 'Jem is in the shower. He said you had left your car near his school and took a cab home? I'll make you some breakfast and you can have the next shower. If you feel halfway decent after that I'll drop you both in on my way to work.'

Miraculously a shower and some food later and I did feel nearly human. Jem found me a new toothbrush and gave me another of his black T-shirts to wear. As we pulled up next to my car he got out and gave me a hug.

'Thank you,' I told him.

'For getting you so drunk you passed out on my couch?' he joked.

'For making me laugh and remember how much fun I used to have with you. Hell, even breaking up with you was the most fun I ever had dumping someone.'

'I'm glad I was helpful,' he said and handed me a piece of paper. 'Here's my number and email address. It was fun seeing you again. If you ever fancy catching up, maybe going to watch a play for old time's sake, do get in touch.'

I kissed his cheek and he pulled me in for a hug. He whispered softly into my ear. 'It's okay to let it go, whatever it is that hurt you.' I pulled back but he continued to talk to me. 'I don't know what you're looking for by going back over the past, but you're obviously still the same crazy fun girl I used to know. Whatever it was, don't make it bigger than it needs to be. You're doing okay.'

I turned to unlock my Mini so that he couldn't see the tears in my eyes. 'I'll call you,' I shouted, as I switched on the engine and drove away. I paused at a corner to wait for a bus to pass, and in my mirror I watched behind me as Jem walked round to Derek's window, reached in and gave him a proper goodbye kiss, and then I drove away too, mulling over his parting words. The peace and contentment that Jem shared with his husband felt contagious. Maybe I should relax and let myself have fun again.

Even though the worst of my hangover had passed, the day still dragged. I set my year sevens to do some silent reading as I hunched over a piece of paper and tried to note down some of the thoughts that were buzzing around in my scattered brain. It wasn't until the second paper aeroplane hit me that I realised that they were as restless and ready for the break as I was. I told them to turn to the person sitting next to them and talk about what they'd just read. We all knew that it was an excuse for them to chat, but they had earned it.

For my year eights, we invented a game where they ran around the playground and when they caught another friend, they had to make up a short story or a poem about something they had seen. Again, as far as I could see they were mostly running talking about *EastEnders* and football, but the gentle breeze was blowing away the last of my headache so it felt like a useful exercise to me.

By the time the final bell rang I felt fully human, but I begged off going to the pub with the other teachers. I planned not to drink again any time soon, and I really wanted to go and visit Jake and see how he was feeling. Jem's pearls of wisdom as we'd said goodbye this morning had left me with butterflies in my stomach. I always enjoyed seeing Jake, he made me feel safe and happy, but as I walked around the corner to knock on his door, I found my mind drifting back to how I'd felt when I had kissed him.

He opened the door wearing denim shorts, an unbuttoned shirt and bare feet. I saw the scattering of blonde curly hair on his chest and completely forgot what I'd meant to say. I hated when guys talked to my chest. Thankfully I rarely had to put up with it, Charmaine on the other hand now owned a T-shirt with an arrow pointing up and the slogan, 'I'm up here' printed on it. Regardless, this time it was me doing the perving. As much as I meant to, I could hardly maintain eye contact.

Jake coughed and drew the edges of his shirt together. 'I gave up on buttons, and given how warm it is today I thought I could get away with it. Perhaps not.'

'Don't cover up on my account,' I spluttered, and even though he'd turned his back to show me into the house I could guess that he was grinning. 'How are you feeling?' I asked as he led me into the kitchen.

'I'm not too bad,' he replied. 'Dad goes home tomorrow, and then I'll be busy looking after Alice again. I think she's enjoyed having Grandpa here this week.'

'Where are they?' I asked, finally noticing how quiet the house seemed.

'Yesterday Alice was pretending to be a T-Rex, so today they're at the Natural History Museum.'

It was one of my favourite places, and normally I'd be able to picture myself walking through the hallowed halls looking at the skeletons and fossils too. Today though I gulped, aware that it was just myself and Jake in the house. The kettle boiled and I jumped out of my seat to make us some tea.

'I can do that,' Jake offered but I shook my head. 'I'm surprised you haven't gone out drinking with all your colleagues,' he said. 'I'd have thought every pub in the country would be full of teachers celebrating tonight.'

'I'm not drinking for a while,' I told him, handing him a mug and running my hand across my forehead, remembering that morning's headache.

He grinned and sat at the table. 'I'm assuming this will be a story worth listening to.'

I paced around the kitchen trying to think where to start. Luckily, before I could, the front door opened and Alice ran in. She threw herself at Jake and began roaring at him. 'I'm a Tyrannosaurus,' she said as she stomped around the room.

Jake's dad sat heavily in a chair and breathed a sigh of relief at being home. Jake crossed to the fridge, grabbed a bottle of lager and handed it to him. Pete twisted the cap off and took a deep drink. 'Now I remember why people have kids when they're your age and not mine,' he told us, looking from me to Jake and back again.

Alice climbed up onto the chair next to her granddad and rested her elbows on the table. 'Dinosaur hungry,' she said, and I assumed this was her hinting that it was time for someone to make her dinner.

'I'm afraid we're all out of triceratops burgers,' Jake said, peering into the freezer. 'But I can offer you some archaeopteryx nuggets and chips, if you like?'

She nodded and he grabbed several packages out of the drawer. Attempting to loosen the clips on the bags, I noticed him wince when he put any pressure on his sore wrist. I got up and walked over to him, taking the bag from his hands and opening it. I saw a flicker of frustration pass across his face, so I gave his hand a gentle squeeze. 'You can cook for me once you're all healed,' I assured him.

'I will,' he replied, giving me a squeeze back and a lingering gaze. His dad coughed gently behind us, and it broke the magnetic force that had held us in place.

'My little T-Rex and I will be next door watching *CBeebies* if you need us,' he said, taking Alice's hand and leading her into the living room.

I raided their fridge again and threw together a quick

pasta dish while the nuggets cooked. I didn't want Bea to get home from work hungry and then have to start cooking.

When Jake went back next door to call them in, his dad was snoring whilst Alice still stalked up and down the room, hunting her prey.

Chapter Twenty

I wanted to find a way to have some time alone with Jake but at the same time my chat with Jem was weighing on my mind. In deciding to try and not be deterred by the past, I became conscious that if I spent time alone with Jake, I wasn't sure what I'd say or do. I shouldn't have worried though. By the time we'd eaten and Alice demanded that Jake read her stories, my day and drunken night were catching up with me and I yawned so loudly than no one questioned me when I said I needed to head home.

My plans to sleep until lunchtime on my first day of holiday were derailed by a ringing sound at nine a.m. I swore loudly and whacked my alarm clock three times before I realised that the noise was actually my doorbell. Throwing on a robe, I went to the door to find Alice and Jake smiling at me.

'We thought we'd give you a lie in,' Jake said as I let them in. He made some coffee while I showered. I found myself taking the time to wash my hair and shave my legs. Partly to point out that I couldn't easily be hurried first thing in the morning, and partly because I found myself wanting to look my best.

I found a loose floaty dress in my wardrobe, feeling quietly pleased with myself that I really was throwing off my jeans and T-shirt habit. I think Jake liked it because I noticed him watching me throughout the day. Alice wanted to go to the park so I spent time pushing her on the swings as Jake's injured wrist wasn't up to the job. We took a picnic and tried to persuade Alice to eat some, even though it was more fun to throw food to the ducks. Afterwards, Jake bought us ice creams and we sat side by side on the edge of the paddling pool, with our feet in the water as we ate.

Alice was tired after her seven hundredth trip down the slide, and insisted that Uncle Jake carry her home. He scooped her up in his good arm and set off down the road. At first he marched off at a good pace, but I could see the effort start to tell. By the time we were safely back in the house with Alice parked in front of *Frozen* on the big TV, and Jake and I sat in the back garden with a glass of lemonade, I could see him grimace and rub his shoulder.

'Cramp,' he muttered through gritted teeth. 'She's getting heavier than I realised.'

I set my glass down and stepped behind him. I started to massage his tender joint, and he sighed as the pain eased. I spread my hands so that they were one on each side of his neck and continued to work his tired muscles. I could feel the strength under my fingers, and even when the last of the tightness appeared to have eased I found myself still touching him.

Eventually he turned and reached for my hands. Guiding me till I was standing in front of him, he placed them flat against his chest and held them in place. I could feel his heart beat under my palm. I felt like I was caught in his gravitational pull, the desire to kiss him was so strong I had to hold myself back. It was clear that he wanted me, and the knowledge gave me a thrill, though I was still held in place by the uncertainty, until his thumb brushed the back of my hand and I came undone. I sat on his knee, trying to avoid bumping into his sore arm, and brushed a soft kiss across his lips.

I kept it light, waiting to see how he would react to me, and he did so by returning my kiss with another, deeper kiss of his own. He gently pulled the scrunchie from my hair and ran his fingers through its auburn length. He nuzzled against my neck and I pressed myself more firmly against his chest. I kissed him again, this time parting my lips and felt his tongue touch mine. I felt a delicious tingle zip down my spine and settle deep within my core.

His hand dropped from my neck to my waist, slowly curving around until it was holding me at the small of my back, pressing me tight against him. The next kiss was so passionate I found myself running my fingertips over his T-shirt, wishing I could remove it and run my hands over his bare chest.

I think Jake felt the same as his fingers ran over the straps of my dress. They slipped down my shoulders and he kissed where they had been. When his hand brushed against my breasts we broke the spell and pulled back, looking into each other's eyes. If Alice hadn't been just metres away I'd have dragged him up to his room there and then.

She was though, and it was just enough to keep me from losing control. I climbed off Jake's lap and he rearranged his shorts as subtly as he could. 'I'd better go,' I said, though I didn't really want to.

'We'll see you tomorrow?' he asked. I nodded and let myself out.

At home I treated myself to a long hot soak in the bath. I didn't sleep well for thinking about how badly I wanted Jake now that I'd allowed myself to think about being with him. Tossing and turning, my bed suddenly felt empty, and I finally fell asleep, imagining how it would have felt to be here in Jake's arms. All too soon my doorbell was ringing again.

Alice greeted me with a bunch of brightly coloured flowers. I kissed the top of her head, and she ran inside my flat. I stepped back so that Jake could enter, then reached behind him to shut the front door. As I did he took me into his arms and kissed me again. I melted against his chest, staying pressed against him until we heard a little voice.

'Yucky kisses,' Alice said, wrinkling her nose at us.

I smiled at her, and saw Jake smile at me. 'What's the plan for today, kiddo?' I asked her.

'Wanna go swimming,' she said.

I looked at the plaster cast on Jake's wrist and told her I'd grab my costume. In my bedroom I found myself trying to decide between the simple black costume that I wore when I swam by myself, and the smaller, brighter bikini which I'd bought for my holiday with Charmaine five years earlier and not worn since.

It was worth rediscovering my bikini line and daring to wear the skimpy outfit, to see Jake's mouth drop open when I led Alice to the pool a little while later. He was sat in the block of spectator seats, high up overlooking the pool and stood up as we walked to the poolside. I turned my back to him as I blew up Alice's armbands and helped her put them on. When I turned back he was still standing. He noticed what he was doing and gave an awkward wave as he sat down. I laughed and blew him a kiss.

Alice and I stayed in the water until our toes were wrinkly, then met Jake in the changing room. He took Alice to get dressed and I went for a shower. I felt his eyes linger on me as I walked away and found myself putting an extra sway in my step for his benefit. Afterwards we went to a café for lunch, but Alice could barely stop yawning.

'I'd better get her home before she falls asleep,' Jake said. 'Bea will kill me if she naps this late because she'll be up until all hours tonight.'

I meant to go back to my flat and get started on the pile of novels I'd been saving up for months to read during the holidays, but instead when Alice asked me to come inside and watch a film with her, I took no persuading. She climbed on to my knee and Jake had to settle for sitting next to me with his arm around me as we watched endless programmes on the *CBeebies* channel.

'I'm going to start the dinner,' Jake said. 'Do you want to stay?'

'I'd love to,' I told him, 'but Charmaine is stopping by later. I haven't caught up with her for a while.'

'She's welcome too,' Jake said so I sent her a text, and curled up with Alice for another show.

Later that evening we were sat round the table, empty plates in front of us, feeling sated and satisfied. For food, at any rate. Alice came in and stood in front us trying to choose who she wanted to read her bedtime stories that night. She looked carefully from her mum, to me and back to Jake. Finally she pointed at him and said, 'Stories, Uncle Jake, but no yucky kisses like you give Evie.'

I felt all the eyes in the house turn to me and I dropped my own eyes to the floor. 'No yucky kisses, I promise,' said Jake, getting up and laughing. He tucked Alice under his arm and disappeared upstairs with her.

'Stories, *please*, young lady,' Bea called after Alice, before she turned back to face me with a questioning look on her face. Bea poured us each a glass of wine. 'It's time that you told us some stories too it seems. How goes the mission? Anything else you want to tell us?'

'I've decided to shelve it,' I announced. I saw Charmaine's eyes go wide, and she didn't speak, but she didn't need to. I could tell what she was thinking. 'I think I've accomplished what I'd needed to,' I told her. 'Seeing some of those guys again brought back memories of how it felt to be carefree, to fall for people without being afraid of getting hurt.'

'How far did you get?' Bea asked me, sipping her drink.

'And no, I don't mean with my brother,' she added with a pretend shudder.

'I'd almost finished with my notebook anyway,' I told them.

I told them about getting drunk with Jem and how sweet he'd been to me. I was just explaining about meeting his husband when Jake came back down saying that Alice was asleep. He fetched himself a drink and sat next to me. I tried to change the subject, feeling suddenly awkward talking about other men in front of him, but Charmaine was enjoying hearing about me waking up hung over and looking awful in front of my ex-boyfriend's gorgeous new partner and wouldn't let me skimp on the details.

'Actually, I just felt happy for him,' I told them all. 'We were never right together, he was so artistic I took it as a licence to act as childishly moody as I wanted, which was fun at the time but I'm so embarrassed now I look back. Seeing him so settled and clearly contented, it was nice.'

'So who would have been next?' Bea asked.

I watched Jake empty his glass and refill it.

'You know what, I'm done with my past. Can't we talk about something else?' I tried.

'You're not that done,' Charmaine reminded me. 'Aren't you coming to the wedding next week?' She raised her eyebrows. 'We get to see how the man you couldn't tame was finally captured.'

Jake choked on his drink and Bea looked at him as she slapped him on his back to help him breathe. 'I'll be there,' I muttered, not meeting his eye.

'I'll look after you,' my cousin assured me. 'I know you were dreading seeing him again.' Charmaine started talking about the new dress she had bought for it, and I tried to keep the subject light, offering to go shoe shopping again. Jake didn't say much, but as most of the talk from then on was about how hard it was to find a dress with decent pockets, the other ladies didn't seem to notice. I did though, and wanted to get him alone to talk. It wasn't to be though. Bea looked exhausted and Charmaine slung her arm over my shoulder. 'Come on, cuz,' she said. 'Let's head off. I've got a busy day tomorrow, fifty people for a three course lunch and we're a chef down.'

I didn't get chance to kiss Jake goodbye, it might have taken a bit more explaining to do so openly in front of Bea and Alice. I missed it though, and once I was back at home on my own, I found myself running my finger gently across my lips and wishing it was Jake.

As I pulled the sheet up around my shoulders and tried to close my eyes, I found sleep elusive. I got up and fetched my mobile. I texted Jake a good night message. I sat up reading for a few minutes in case he wrote back, but he didn't.

Chapter Twenty-One

The next morning there was no ring on my doorbell to get me out of bed. I tried to enjoy having the day to myself, pretending that the space was what I wanted. I finally had a sort out; doing the jobs that always ended getting put off until my holidays. I put aside bags of old clothes and books to take to the charity shop. The one drawback of having such a small flat was the constant need to keep on top of my desire to hoard.

By lunchtime I'd also been for a haircut and written long overdue emails to overseas friends. I wanted to make lunch, but it seemed that a trip to the supermarket was next on my to-do list, when my empty fridge made a mockery of my plans. I grabbed my car keys and headed for the door.

It only took me twenty minutes to find everything I needed. I treated myself to a ready-made sandwich to take home. Having bought the groceries, I could no longer face actually cooking with them.

Back at my flat, I found myself emptying cupboards and scrubbing them as I packed away the shopping. It was no use though, I couldn't distract myself. Once the last item was safely put away, I picked up my keys and walked round to Jake's before I could think about what I was going to say or get nervous about what he might.

Alice cheered when she saw me, and I was glad that someone was pleased to see me. I handed her the bag of cake ingredients and she danced back into the kitchen, chattering as she went about the super duper triple layer melty goo cake she wanted to make. Jake kissed my cheek as I walked in. It wasn't the passionate kiss like the ones we'd shared the day before, but at least it was a gesture of affection.

We didn't get chance to talk until the cakes were baking in the oven. Alice asked if they were ready yet every thirty seconds until Jake chased her out of the room. He came back in a few minutes later explaining that he had set her the challenge of drawing a picture of what her cake would look like once we'd decorated it.

He put the kettle on and I began picking up the dirty mixing bowls and stacking them in the dishwasher. I must have clunked them louder than I meant to, as by the time I got to the third bowl, Jake took it from my hands, put it away himself and put his arms around me. He placed a gentle kiss on my lips, and I laid my head against his shoulder.

'I'm sorry if I was grumpy with you,' he offered.

'It's hard to be grumpy when you haven't said a word,' I told him.

'I know,' he said, running his hand through his hair. 'I knew about you tracking down your exes, of course. It's just that the closer I got to you, the less I wanted to think about you with other people. Especially the ones who left you feeling that you didn't deserve to be happy.'

'George was never one of those,' I assured him. 'Besides, in case you hadn't noticed, I came away from each of those encounters being more sure than ever about why it hadn't worked with each of them. Not to mention that if I hadn't started I'd never have met you in the first place.'

He blew out a sigh and kissed me again. 'I'm being silly, and possessive, and a tiny bit caveman, I know.'

'A tiny bit?' I said and grinned to show him that I was just teasing. 'But for what it's worth, I decided that I don't need to track down any more people,' I told him. 'I feel more confident than I have in ages. Look, I'm even wearing short shorts, despite my knobbly knees.'

'I'd noticed the shorts,' Jake said, kissing me more deeply this time.

'Though there is one thing I should probably mention,' I said, not wanting to break the spell but neither wanting to make peace with Jake only to have to recover the same ground three days later. 'I have to go to a wedding on Saturday.'

'The one Charmaine mentioned?' he asked.

I nodded. 'It's another ex, but before you say anything, I can't really get out of going. My parents will be expecting me to be there and I never told them about George, so it'll look a little odd now if I pull out at the last minute.'

'Do I want to know about him?' Jake asked.

I shook my head again. 'Probably not,' I admitted. 'It was over a long time ago, but he's my brother Matt's best friend.' Jake actually grinned at that. 'I know,' I told him, 'it's a stereotype, a girl and her brother's best friend. But no happy ever afters from this one.'

After I broke up with Jem, I'd been happy to stay single for a while. I wasn't proud of myself for acting so childishly with him and had resolved to take some time out from dating to figure out what I wanted. Truthfully, it wasn't hard to stay single, I wasn't exactly overwhelmed by offers.

So I didn't date again for a few months. By the summer holidays I felt calmer, had started researching teacher-training courses for after I finished my degree, but was starting to have an itch that only an encounter could scratch, if you know what I mean. Charmaine suggested trying a one-night stand, but that wasn't really my style. I found my thoughts drifting back to George more and more often. I wondered whether he'd mind being a booty call.

It wasn't hard to find out. I simply invited myself along

on a night out with Matt, got myself dressed up in my shortest skirt and smallest top. It took Matt an hour to disappear off with the girl that he was dating that week, and within an hour and a half George and I were back at his flat and I was feeling satisfied.

That summer I invited myself out with them a few more times, and each trip followed the same pattern. George and I even started swapping texts and meeting up when we could do without drawing attention to ourselves. Charmaine warned me that it was purely physical for George, and even though we didn't go on actual dates, we spent so much time talking afterwards as we snuggled, that I could no longer stop myself from falling, and falling hard, for him. My other friends had drifted off to college or to work, and he was a fun way to fill the gap they had left. With hindsight, I could see that I had relied on him too much, more than he had agreed to. And I'd needed him far more than he had needed me.

When I turned down a going for a drink with a really nice guy from my course, Charmaine had tried to talk sense into me, but it hadn't worked. Thankfully she didn't bear a grudge, and even more luckily she was with me the day the shit hit the fan.

The four of us had been talking about going to a gig for ages, and we'd finally got round to booking the tickets. We were meeting at George's flat, and I'd had a giggle pretending to not know where anything was and almost going into the bedroom whilst looking for the bathroom.

Charmaine gave me a warning look, but I couldn't help myself. Until Matt went into George's room to borrow some aftershave and came out carrying a jacket I must have dropped. 'Don't you have one like this, sis?' he asked me.

'Must be a popular style,' I muttered, trying not to blush

and probably failing. That's the trouble with having ginger hair, I'm also pale and what would be the smallest hint of a red cheek on anyone else would practically glow in the dark on me.

'Funny how this one smells of the same perfume you wear,' he said, handing it to me. I took it quietly. 'Is there something you want to tell me?' he asked. 'Only, I picked it up and there was a bra underneath.'

I shook my head and George tried to placate him. 'It's not what it looks like,' he said.

Matt's eyes widened, and he obviously twigged that it was exactly what it looked like.

'You fucking bastard,' he yelled at George, backing him up against the wall. 'That's my little sister.'

I tried to intervene and push him away but he was too strong.

'I'm twenty years old,' I pointed out.

'You're still way too young and way too nice to go near him,' he growled at me, placing his elbow across George's neck. I grew scared that he might really hurt him and I realised how stupid I'd been.

'You go out and screw whoever you want. Why can't I do the same? You're being sexist,' I pointed out but he didn't react at all to my words. 'I don't need a protector,' I shouted, trying again to get him to release George. 'Please, Matt, don't hurt him. I really care about him.'

Matt finally pulled back, letting George drop to his knees and draw in a proper breath. 'You care about him?' he asked. I nodded. 'Then you probably wouldn't want to know that he's also been shagging Sharon from the Red Lion for the last three weeks as well.'

His words hit me like a physical blow, but probably still not as hard as the punch that he delivered to George's stomach.

Matt stalked out of the flat. 'I'll follow him,' Charmaine said.

I helped George to sit and fetched him an ice pack for his bruises. 'I should probably find him and apologise too,' George said.

I wondered why I didn't rate an apology, but George had never promised me anything, and he clearly didn't realise how attached to him I'd felt. I started crying and he still didn't reach out to comfort me, just shoved a box of tissues across the table at me.

Matt and George didn't speak to each other for a month after that. I felt guilty about coming between them, but eventually they patched things up. I don't know how, I guess they just decided not to talk about what had happened. I was hurt about how it had ended between us. I missed George, both physically and as a friend. We never went to bed together again. To this day I'd never said more than another dozen words to him. And now in three days' time I had to go to his wedding.

Chapter Twenty-Two

I bought myself a short, lacy black dress to wear to the wedding. It wasn't a traditional choice of clothing, but dressed up with a golden shawl and necklace, it made me feel really good when I tried it on and I knew I'd need that. I even let Charmaine talk me into buying a pair of proper heels. I wasn't sure how I'd walk in them, but I guessed I'd either manage somehow or get so drunk that I wouldn't care either way. Charmaine asked me whether I was in mourning, given that I was wearing black, but my head was full of thoughts of Jake, and I was pretty sure that I wasn't.

The night before the wedding, we were both having dinner with Jake and Bea again when Charmaine's mobile rang. Disappearing outside to answer it, she came back looking really cross. 'Men,' she grunted, then, 'No offence,' as she looked up at Jake.

'None taken,' he said, getting up to offer her more garlic bread.

'What happened?' I asked.

'Jason, the guy I've been seeing from the wine suppliers, was supposed to get tomorrow off to come with me. Only the stupid git just rang to tell me he forgot to clear it with his boss and now he has to work. Great, now I'll look like a knobby no mates with an empty seat next to me all day.' Charmaine was not used to being short of a date.

'Jake can go with you,' Bea offered, as we all turned to look at her. 'It makes sense, no use them paying for a meal that gets wasted. They'll have the table plans printed up and everything so Jake can just take his seat. I'm off tomorrow anyway and it would be lovely to have a quiet day with Alice.'

'That's decided then,' Jake said, picking up his juice glass and clinking it against mine. 'Looks like I'll be coming with you ladies to the wedding.'

I turned down Jake's offer to walk us home, and as soon as the door shut behind us I turned to my cousin. 'This isn't going to be awkward at all, is it? Turning up to the wedding with another man.'

'It'll be good for you,' she assured me. 'Think how much stronger you'll feel when George sees that you've brought someone with you. And a gorgeous guy at that.'

'He is a bit gorgeous, isn't he?' I said, finally cracking a smile.

Charmaine promised to be round early the next morning to fix my hair and make-up. I didn't think I'd sleep well, but knowing I'd have a knock out outfit and a man on my arm left me feeling so relaxed that I did manage to conk out after all.

Charmaine arrived wearing a vivid pink dress, far brighter than I could have ever worn, but it suited her. She twirled and I told her that she looked amazing. 'I know,' she responded, then announced that it was my turn to get ready. 'So what is the story with you and Jake?' she asked me as I got dressed.

'I like him,' I said, admitting it to her and to myself. 'I really like him. He makes me feel amazing, he makes me laugh. I love how his eyes linger when he watches me. He makes me feel sexy.'

'You are sexy,' she said.

'I don't think so,' I scoffed.

'Being sexy is a state of mind,' she said, strutting up and down my flat, as much as you can strut in the three paces she could fit in before turning like a catwalk model.

'I think that's been my trouble. My state of mind wasn't under my control for a long time.'

'But you got it back,' she pointed out. 'So let's get you made up, and show George what he missed out on.'

'I think I'd prefer to show Jake what he can have,' I said. 'I think I may have done enough looking backwards now.'

'That sounds even better,' Charmaine said, picking up my hairbrush and starting to work the knots out of my long hair. We experimented with it tied back in a loose plait, then with it down. Eventually Charmaine curled it so that it hung in gentle waves. She painted my lips in red saying that I'd need a little contrast against my simple dress, and found a green eye shadow that complimented the colour of my eyes.

When she had finished she finally let me look in the full-length mirror in my room. I was amazed at what she'd created.

'Is that really me?' I asked her, swishing my dress from side to side to see how it flew when I moved.

'Sexy, I told you,' she said. 'Self-assured and, most of all, happy. I can see it on your face.'

'Thank you, hon,' I told her. 'I love you so much. I couldn't have done this without you. Not any of it, not starting over again, finding my flat, meeting Jake. I owe you.' I turned and gave her a hug.

'Careful not to smudge,' she warned me. I could see she was trying not to say anything soppy herself. 'You deserve this. You're a good person, Evie, and nothing that happened, not with any of the losers that you looked up, none of that was down to you.'

'Some of it was,' I said, and I found my eyes welling up. She shook her head, and I figured I was in for a lecture about protecting my mascara too but luckily the doorbell rang. She went to let Jake in. He whistled when he saw her and she faked a punch to his good arm, but I knew she was secretly pleased. I wondered what he would say when he saw me, but he simply shook his head from side to side and grinned.

'Okay?' I asked.

'Better than okay,' he said, crossing the room and taking me into his arms. He began to kiss me but Charmaine coughed from the doorway.

'No smudging. I told you,' she said. 'That lipstick took me ages to get right and to stop Evie biting it off, so you leave it be, at least until everyone has seen her in it.'

Jake saluted her and held out his good arm for me to take. 'Shall we?' he asked. I nodded, and let him lead me out to the taxi.

My parents were waiting outside the church, and Mum kissed my cheek as she greeted me.

'I never thought I'd see the day a woman tried to tame that boy,' she said, shaking her head. I wondered what she'd think if she knew I'd once dreamt that I could be that woman. Instead I introduced her to Jake. I didn't know how to describe him. He was certainly more than a friend, but we hadn't formally dated, and it felt too presumptuous to call him my boyfriend. I simply gave them each other's names and started to walk inside the building. Jake reached for me and intertwined his fingers in mine. I saw my mum notice, but before I could say anything, she simply gave me a small nod and smile, and followed us in.

The church was several hundred years old, and the history of the building, alongside the stained glass windows and beautiful wooden pews leant an additional majesty to the ceremony. The service was heartfelt, and when Zoe said her vows, promising to love George forever because he was her best friend, I found my eyes filling up not with jealousy, but with happiness for them both.

I hoped Jake wouldn't notice, but of course he did. Once the official bits were done, and George and Zoe had kissed to the delight of the crowd, we filed back outside. The photographer called various groups of people together to take photos, and I found myself walking further away, around the other side of the church and out into the small graveyard behind it.

I read the headstones, noticing how young so many of the people buried here had been, and how many of the stones set out the relationships and emotions of those left behind. 'Deeply missed', 'beloved wife of', and 'forever in our hearts'. I wondered if I would ever mean that much to one person, to be their happily ever after.

'Are you okay?' said a voice behind me. I turned to see Jake watching me. I nodded and he walked over, holding his arms out so that I could bury myself against him for a hug. 'I wasn't sure if you needed time by yourself, in case you were grieving today.' He nodded back towards the church building. 'Charmaine sent me to check on you. I wasn't sure if you'd want me to, but she said you would. And I really do want to help you if I can.'

That snapped me out of my funk and made me smile again. 'I wasn't sad for myself, honestly,' I told him, pressing myself tighter against him. 'George and I were over a long time ago, and in truth we were never going to be a proper couple. He never thought of me that way, and I think I knew too much about his past behaviours, I should never have expected more. I'm not sure I could have ever fully trusted him, though I hope for his wife's sake that he really has changed.'

'So you're not feeling like you missed out?' he said, bending his head to look me straight in the eye.

I assured him that I didn't. It said a lot about his character that he could wonder whether I was still mourning the loss of an ex-partner and still come to check up on me. 'I was just wondering whether I could ever mean as much to someone else as these people obviously once did.' I pointed out the inscriptions I'd been reading.

'You mean a lot to me,' he said, kissing my lips.

'You mean a lot to me too,' I said into his chest. 'More than George ever did. The invite might have kick-started my mission, but he wasn't the one who left me questioning myself. If anything he tried to give me the confidence to feel like a woman, it's just that back then I didn't realise that he didn't mean as his woman.'

He stepped back to watch me as I talked, but just at that moment Charmaine entered the graveyard and called out to us. 'They want the whole wedding party for the next few photos,' she said. We followed her back around, stepping carefully to walk around the graves and not step on them. When I wobbled in my heels Jake's steady arm shot out and held me up. The strength in his biceps took my mind off my sombre thoughts, and I held on to him tighter than I needed to.

Chapter Twenty-Three

We were seated at round tables in the hotel's main ballroom. Oversized wine glasses contained mini rose plants, the petals the same colour as Zoe's bouquet and the bridesmaids' dresses. A few little kids were running around blowing bubbles, and I tried my best to eat the meal despite the tension in the pit of my stomach.

'This should be interesting,' said my dad, sitting back with his glass of sparkling wine and waiting for Matt to begin his best man's speech. Zoe looked radiant in her white strapless gown. The tiara sat proudly against her blonde hair, and she couldn't keep the smile from her face. Neither could her mum. The tiny woman was sat next to her on the top table, and they held hands as Zoe's dad gave the father of the bride speech. Eventually he finished telling us the multitude of growing up stories, and raised his glass for the toast. Neither of them looked nervous waiting for the best man's speech. Had they really got no idea of the stories my brother could tell about George?

I had to remind myself to save some wine for after Matt had spoken, and not to down it all now as I wanted to. Matt stood, and I felt my face blush as red as my lipstick. Charmaine kicked me under the table, and I caught her eye. She mimed taking a deep, calming breath, and I tried to copy her lead. Jake held my hand, and I had to pull mine back for a moment first so I could wipe it on my napkin to try and hide from him how sweaty my palms were.

'I know it is customary to regale you all with tales of George's sordid past,' Matt began, and I held my breath. Surely my own brother wouldn't out me in front of the entire crowd. 'But we'd be here all night, and now that George has managed to persuade Zoe to marry him, I don't want to scare her off, so I'll save those tales for another time.'

I breathed a sigh of relief, and when everyone at my table, my parents included, turned to look at me, I knew I should have been a bit quieter. The rest of the crowd laughed, and I tried to let my tension flow away. Matt proceeded to talk about how drunk George had got on his stag night and how they had tied him naked to a picnic table on the beach. I was glad that Matt had no shortage of embarrassing stories that didn't include other women.

Eventually the speeches were over, the tables were cleared and we waited outside in the bar whilst the big room was reset for the evening reception. 'I'm going to freshen up,' Charmaine said, dipping into her bag to find the key to her room.

'I think I'll do the same,' I said. Jake downed the rest of his pint and came with us. We fetched our overnight bags from where we'd left them in the lobby and walked up the carpeted hall. As we stood next to the two rooms, we faced another dilemma. Charmaine had booked a double room, expecting to be here with a guy. I'd booked a single, and now there were three of us wondering who would be sleeping in each room.

'I can take the single, if you guys want to share?' Jake offered.

'No offence, but have you heard her snore?' Charmaine said, pointing at me. She grabbed the key to the single room from my fingers and handed me the one she had held. Then she let herself in and closed the door before I could respond.

'Looks like we're in here then,' Jake said, taking the key from my hand and opening the door. He came back for our bags and dropped them on the floor by the bed. The one big inviting bed which dominated the room. I still hadn't said a word, so Jake rested his hands on my shoulders. 'I can sleep on the floor, if you need me to,' he offered.

I shook my head, and found the courage that I'd been slowly rebuilding over the last few months. Reaching behind me, I undid the zip of my dress and dropped it to the ground. Stepping out of it, wearing just my red knickers and heels, I stepped back towards the bathroom. 'I think I'll take a quick shower,' I told him. I could see his Adam's apple bobbing up and down.

As I switched the shower on and waited for it to warm up, I tried not to look behind me as I waited to see how he would react. As I stepped into the tub Jake finally stepped into the room too.

'Damn that shower looks good,' he said.

'Come in and join me?' I suggested.

He held up his arm and I remembered the cast on his wrist. 'I can't, not for another three weeks. But it's just gone to the top of the list of things I want to do when this comes off,' he said, his voice thick with arousal. He stood, leaning against the door frame as I stayed under the spray. I took my time under the water, then washed carefully and thoroughly with the foamy shower gel. When I soaped my chest for the second time, his hand shot into the cubicle and turned the water off.

'You're torturing me on purpose,' he said, lifting me out and wrapping a big fluffy towel around me. I threw my arms around his neck and kissed my way down his jawline. Walking backwards towards the bed, I drew him with me. Once the back of my knees hit the mattress, I laid myself down gently on it, and Jake covered me with his body.

We ignored Charmaine when she banged on the door

to say she was going back to the reception. We missed the first dance, and when we finally got dressed and went back, I noticed my mum giving me a sharp look. I didn't care. Jake held me in his arms, and we danced together underneath the glitter ball, which hung from the ceiling. Eventually my feet began to ache from my stupid shoes, and I begged for a break.

Jake led me to a round table at the back of the room, kissed me in the candlelight and went to the bar to fetch me a drink. Matt threw himself into the seat next to me. 'Thanks, Matt,' I said.

'What for?' he asked, though I was sure he knew.

'Not embarrassing me in your speech earlier,' I reminded him.

'No offence, Evie, but it wasn't the most sensible thing you ever did. I didn't really want to let everyone here know you had been so stupid as to go near him.'

'You were every bit as bad as he was,' I pointed out.

'But I wanted better for you, little sis,' he said, not looking at me. 'It's good to see you getting over the bastard.' Gesturing with his beer bottle at where Jake was stood at the bar, he said, 'He treats you the way you deserve to be treated.'

'He does,' I agreed, thinking of how Jake had been so gentle, tender and oh, so thorough in our room earlier. 'But George was never that much of a bastard to me. Not really. He never lied to me. I did that to myself.'

'I wasn't talking about George,' he said, emptying his bottle and standing up. 'So, which bridesmaid do you think I have the best shot with?' he asked, weaving his way back on to the dance floor.

Jake came back with a couple of bottles of lager. We sat drinking them quietly, side by side, holding hands and watching Matt work his magic on the maid of honour. He span her round slowly, then dipped her in his arms. A few quiet whispers in her ear later and the two of them slipped from the room.

'He is incorrigible,' I muttered in disbelief.

'I don't know,' Jake said, nuzzling my neck. 'There is something pretty romantic about weddings, don't you think?'

I watched my parents hold hands and walk together onto the dance floor.

'Do you believe in happy ever afters?' I asked Jake as we watched the happy couple slow dance around the floor. I'd been worried beforehand that it might be awkward if George and I made eye contact, but as I saw him unable to look away from his new wife, I realised that I needn't have worried.

'I didn't use to,' he admitted. 'My parents split up when I was five, and Dad did a good job bringing us up, but I was left feeling a bit sceptical about marriage. I pushed some of that aside when Bea got married. She was so happy. Until she wasn't. Truthfully, I wasn't even looking for a partner, then I met you and now I can't stop hoping that forever is even possible.'

I took his hand and led him back to our room. 'Let's start ours right now,' I told him.

Chapter Twenty-Four

Making it through the wedding in one piece had left my nerves ragged. I hadn't expected to sleep well afterwards but Jake's arms helped soothe me. It was a new kind of heaven. He held me pressed against his bare chest with his uninjured arm. I woke up to find our legs entwined and his face buried in my hair. I pulled the sheet up to cover myself, but he swept it back aside. He whispered in my ear that I was beautiful, and then kissed away the tears as they fell from my eyes. We made love again, and he didn't stop talking to me, the whole way through, caressing my heart with his words.

Jake fell asleep again afterwards, and I lay against him, feeling the gentle sway of his breathing. I couldn't drop off again myself, and eventually I began to feel restless. When he hadn't stirred after my shower, I got dressed, left him a note and wandered downstairs in search of coffee.

The breakfast was set out in the same large ballroom the reception had been held in the night before. The staff had obviously been busy, the disco ball was gone, as were the balloons and flowers. Instead, dozens of small tables were set out, each covered in a pristine white cloth and polished cutlery.

I could smell the bacon and despite being a long-term vegetarian, I found my stomach was rumbling. A waiter greeted me at the door and let me choose where I wanted to sit. Most of the wedding guests had not emerged yet, so I had pretty much the pick of the room. There were a couple of families with small children. The kids looked excited at being able to choose from so many options for breakfast. Their parents all looked exhausted, and I thought of Bea and Alice. I smiled at the parents but chose a seat far away. Maybe once I'd had my caffeine I could be more sociable.

A young waitress brought me a small white china cup of coffee. She motioned to show me that the milk and sugar were already on the table, but I told her I'd drink it black and asked if I could have more please. Two refills later and my stomach rumbled again, gently reminding me that it had woken up a while ago and wanted feeding now.

I loaded a plate with pastries. I thought about grabbing a yogurt and pretending to be healthy, but then I spotted the waffles and knew that if I had any room left I'd be going back for those instead. Jake and I had probably worked off a few hundred calories overnight so I figured I'd earned them. Besides, I deserved some treats for getting through this weekend.

I smiled to myself as I sat down, daydreaming about how I'd dreaded facing George at his wedding, and that instead I'd spent the night with a wonderful man. All those weeks earlier when the invite had dropped onto my mat and left me shaken, I could never have foreseen how life would play out. In fact, had it not been for the invite I might never have met Jake. A hand landed on my shoulder, and I turned round ready to greet my new man. Instead I jumped when I saw George standing there.

'Sorry, I didn't mean to scare you,' he said.

'You didn't,' I mumbled, hiding my face behind my coffee cup. 'I wasn't expecting to see you.'

'It is my wedding,' he pointed out, laughing gently at my obvious discomfort.

I kicked the chair out so that he could sit opposite me if he wanted to. He did, and the waitress came back to take his order of tea. 'Did you and your wife not have plans for the morning then?' I asked.

'Already taken care of,' he said, winking at me. I thought

I'd be more embarrassed talking about sex with him, but it turns out that knowing that I had left a naked man in my room upstairs made me feel much more at peace and I surprised myself by smiling back. 'Zoe wanted a lie in so she sent me out. She thought it was polite for one of us to be here to greet our guests. Only they're a sensible bunch and they've decided to sleep in too. Apart from you.'

It was the longest conversation we had had in years, and he wasn't done yet. His tea arrived and he thanked the waitress. I noticed her checking him out as she approached. The old George would have clocked this instantly and switched on the charm. Zoe must have been something special though as he ignored her, if he was aware of her attention at all.

George took a sip of his tea, and his eyes followed his hand, staring at his wedding ring. 'I wonder how long it is going to take me to get used to that,' he said.

'You look as though you're surprised to be married,' I said.

'You'd think the year of planning would have left me prepared, wouldn't you?'

'Don't tell me you're not,' I remarked, sitting back and looking at him.

He shook his head. 'No, I'm fine,' he assured me. 'I never thought of myself as the settling down type, but then I met Zoe and it turns out I am.'

'You looked very happy together,' I said, taking a bite of my Danish pastry. The crumbs fell all over my jeans, and for a moment I wished I'd also packed a kick arse outfit for today too. For all of my planning, I'd never expected to be sitting here facing George the morning after he got married.

'She's beautiful. I never thought I'd get so lucky, having such a sweet girl care about me so much.' I didn't know how to reply to that so I sat silently and carried on eating. 'Ah damn, Evie,' he said. 'I didn't mean it like that.'

'I know,' I assured him. 'And I'm fine. It was a long time ago. And like you said, back then we never made any promises to each other.' He shuffled his feet and I wondered whether he knew how much I'd cared about him. Whilst he must have been fond of me to spend so much time together, and to have listened to me and supported me, it was only now that I had Jake that I realised what love truly was, and how far from that my feelings for him had really been.

'You seem well sorted yourself. I saw the guy you were with yesterday. He looked pretty sweet on you.'

I felt my cheeks flush. I'd never been able to hide my emotions, and George knew me too well to even try. 'It's pretty new,' I told him, 'but I like him. I really like him.'

All the years and all the distance seemed to fade away, and it felt good to be talking to my old friend again.

'So are you doing what I always told you? Showing the world it ought to sit up and watch you?'

I grinned, remembering how I'd so often come away from my time with him feeling on top of the world. 'I lost that for a while,' I admitted. 'I'm doing my best to get it back though.'

George finished his tea and got up. 'I promised Zoe I'd wait for her to have breakfast,' he said, pushing his chair back under the table. He leant over and kissed my cheek. Once, a long time ago, that would have sent butterflies to my stomach. Today, it felt like a goodbye. He turned to walk away and I called his name again.

'I just wanted to thank you,' I told him when he looked back. 'You were a good friend when I needed one. You were gentle, kind, and you taught me a lot about who I wanted to be.'

He sat back down quickly and stared at his shoes. 'You say thank you, I still feel like I should be saying sorry. You were a kid, you were my mate's sister. I never meant to hurt you.'

'I chose to get involved with you. In fact, half of what we got up to was because I started it,' I told him. He looked off in the distance and I wondered if he was thinking back to some of our more innocent and intimate times together. 'Besides, I'm happy with where I'm at now. I wasn't for a long time, but I've been thinking about what you used to say to me a lot recently. If it wasn't for what we did, I wouldn't be here with Jake right now, so I'm grateful to you, really.'

He reached out, gave my hand a squeeze then wandered off to find his bride.

My parents came in a moment later with Matt, but there was no sign of his bridesmaid from the night before. I wondered what Matt would have done if he'd seen George and me talking a moment earlier. Would he have assumed that we were trying to hook up again? Though the thought hadn't even crossed my mind. Would he have trusted us to find our peace as we had?

I had almost finished my coffee when Jake strode into the room. He greeted me with a kiss, not embarrassed to do so in front of my family. I took his hand under the table and I didn't let go.

Chapter Twenty-Five

We found our own little routine after that, taking Alice out during the day, having tea ready for when Bea got home from work, then Jake would walk me home. More often than not he would stay over. I wasn't sure whether Bea was ready for us to explain my presence in the mornings to Alice, so mostly it felt easier that way, waking up in the morning and rushing to get back before Bea had to leave again. She seemed happy to see us together, but I didn't want to flaunt our relationship in her face when she was still grieving for her own broken marriage. After cutting it fine for a few days in a row, Jake asked me if I would consider staying at his house.

The matter was decided the following Friday night when my boiler went on the blink. Having been to the library, the park and the toy shop in thirty-degree heat, when I couldn't have my bath I lost it slightly. I packed a bag and told Jake we were going to his. With hindsight I probably hadn't needed to bring a whole suitcase for one night, but I hadn't wanted to use all of Bea's bubble bath, so I'd packed all of my own bottles and pots, alongside my big fluffy towel for afterwards, my hair dryer, and just a small selection of clothes.

'How many days are you staying for?' he joked.

'It depends whether my landlord continues to be so bloody useless,' I told him. 'Last winter he left me without heating for three weeks before he got the boiler fixed. At least I don't need to worry about freezing my bollocks off this time.' Jake stared at me, then wisely decided not risk my temper by commenting on how my terminology didn't match my anatomy. I'm not at my most patient when my feet ache and I'm coated in that stickiness you get from being active so much on a hot day. Instead he took my bag.

'I get the feeling you need a long soak, and maybe a glass of wine,' he said, laughing until he saw my glare. 'Okay, note to self, stereotypes about redhead temper are justified.' I glared at him. 'They are also not a joking matter.' He carried my bag in silence, let me in and guided me up the stairs, saying that he would explain to Bea. I don't think he trusted me to speak until I'd had half an hour in the tub. I was on my third helping of hot water when there was a delicate knock on the door and Jake let himself in.

'Bea says she took the lock off the door so that Alice couldn't lock herself in. I hated it the first time I was trying to use the loo and Alice burst in on me, but now I'm starting to see her point,' he said.

'I think you're looking at my points,' I said, sliding my chest back underneath the bubble so that Jake could meet my eyes again. He handed me a glass of wine. I took a sip, sighed in pleasure and apologised for being grumpy earlier. Picking up my towel, Jake helped me out of the bath and led me to his room. He gave me one of those back massages that soothe your weary soul as much as your tired muscles, and even though I could see how much he was enjoying running his hands over me, I still managed to fall asleep before we could do anything about it.

In the morning I woke up to find Jake stood in front of me wearing just his pyjama bottoms, holding out a mug of coffee. I sat up and reached for it, drinking half before I managed to speak again. 'It should have been me treating you to a cuppa in bed, and apologising again for my mood yesterday.'

He took the mug from my hands, set it down on his bedside table and climbed back into bed next to me. 'Don't worry,' he reassured me, 'we all have bad days sometimes. Alice says she needs croissants for breakfast. Bea talked to her for ten minutes but nothing else would do so they've gone to the café.' He started kissing my neck and I realised what he actually meant.

'How long will they be out?' I asked.

'Not long,' he admitted. 'They went a few minutes ago. I wanted to wake you up earlier but you looked so peaceful. I just wanted to let you sleep as long as I could. I really appreciate how much of your holiday you've given up to help us.' He gestured to his injured arm.

'It was my pleasure,' I reassured him. 'I've really enjoyed spending this time with Alice.' He raised an eyebrow at me. 'And with you, of course,' I said, smiling at him and admiring the scattering of golden hair that curled in the centre of his muscular chest. He resumed kissing me, and I found my body waking up.

'Do you think we've got time? What happens if they get back before we finish?' I asked.

'If you manage to keep the volume down I think we could get away with it,' he said.

I painted a shocked look on my face. 'Are you saying I'm loud in bed?' I asked him, knowing full well that he was telling the truth. Lying back and doing his best Meg Ryan impression, Jake demonstrated what he thought I sounded like. Straddling him and reaching over into his bedside drawer for a condom, I said, 'You set a high standard for yourself, mister. You'd better make me make those noises for real or I'm going to put in a complaint.'

Running his hands over me again, Jake did his best to comply.

'Don't get me wrong,' he said afterwards as we lay side by side panting, 'I love hearing what I do to you.'

'I love it too,' I said, carefully skirting the words I found myself wanting to say to him. I wasn't sure if he was ready yet to hear the three-word refrain that was skipping across my mind more and more often when I was with him. We heard the front door slam shut and a moment later Alice's voice was calling us from outside the bedroom door. Jake reached for his clothes, and dropping one more kiss on my shoulder, he got dressed and got up to play super uncle again. I meant to get up and help too, but found myself closing my eyes and promising myself just five more minutes in bed.

This time when I woke up it was to find Alice peering at me, with her face just two inches from mine. 'Lunchtime, Aunt Evie,' she said, looking very serious.

I got up, brushed my teeth and pulled my hair back into a ponytail. I found a loose cotton skirt in my bag and a vest top. It promised to be another hot day.

'Sorry,' I said as I sat at the table next to Jake. 'I don't know why I'm so tired today.'

'You've had a busy week looking after my munchkin,' Bea said, sliding a plate of beans on toast in front of me. 'I wasn't sure what meal you'd be ready for, breakfast or lunch, so we've made a brunch.' Jake was adding tomato ketchup to his bacon sandwich and Alice was tucking into a bowl of scrambled eggs.

'This is just what I needed,' I said. 'What is the plan for the afternoon?'

Bea explained that there was a film that Alice wanted to see at the cinema. I didn't really fancy watching animated teddy bears for two hours, but the lure of air conditioning was too good to miss so I offered to take her. Jake sighed, realising that his afternoon of relaxing had disappeared, but when Alice offered to share her popcorn, he grinned and I knew that he didn't mind really. Bea looked relieved at the idea of having a couple of hours at home by herself, so after we finished eating we piled into my car and I drove us to the shopping centre where the cinema was located on the top floor.

We were sat in the dark of the cinema, and just as the trailers started to play, I felt my stomach begin to cramp. The mystery of why I'd been so tired and grumpy the day before was solved. I should have known what was coming. I reached for my handbag, and realised that I'd left my usual supplies at home. Telling Jake I'd be back in a minute, I dashed to the loos, but predictably their sanitary towel machine was broken.

I didn't want to risk sitting in a pale skirt for two hours with no protection, so I grabbed my purse and left the cinema. I flew down the escalator, dashed down the mall and found a pharmacy. Running around as quickly as possible, I couldn't spot what I needed anywhere. Normally every other aisle seems to be labelled with the polite and somewhat mild description of feminine hygiene products. In the end I grabbed the first shop assistant I could see, who happened of course to be about sixteen and male, and asked him where the tampons were. He pointed directly behind me, so I thanked him, blushed, and grabbed a packet of pads.

The queue at the till was barely moving. I got stuck behind a little old lady who insisted on paying with exactly the right coins, and a middle-aged man who wanted to be sure that the shampoo he was buying was the one his wife would find acceptable. I don't know how the cashier kept her temper, I was rapidly losing mine. I tried to pay as quickly as I could, refusing the offer of a bag, turning down the new store card that was proffered, and running back to the cinema.

I tried to find which pocket I'd put my ticket stub in for safekeeping, but thankfully the young lady who was checking the tickets took pity on me. Perhaps they didn't often get redheads running around like nutters and she remembered me from my speedy exit. Regardless, she let me back in, and I stopped at the loo, opened my purchase and got myself cleaned up.

As I sat back down next to Jake and Alice, Jake whispered in my ear to ask what was wrong. Alice told him to stop talking, and I was glad of the chance to rest without being able to talk so that I could get my breath back.

Chapter Twenty-Six

Jake was so sweet. When I finally had chance to explain about why I'd run out on him, he turned a little pale. I think he was worried about how much detail I was going to go into. He settled me on the sofa with a book and a cup of tea, as if he was worried that I was going to break. I wanted to point out that I'd been coping with periods on my own for the last fifteen years, but it was very comforting to be fussed over.

Charmaine had nipped round whilst we were out and we came back to find that she was giving Bea a quick tutorial in the kitchen. The smells were amazing and I hoped that they were also making a veggie version of whatever they were cooking up. Charmaine took one look at me lying down feeling sorry for myself and shook her head. 'Time of the month?' she asked. I nodded. 'Poor Jake,' she said. 'He has no idea what a world of trouble he's in for this week.'

I picked up a cushion and was about to throw it at her when I realised that this would prove her correct. Instead I plumped it up and set it back behind me. She laughed and disappeared back out of the room again.

Jake popped his head around the door to ask if I wanted him to bring my dinner in on a tray but I reassured him that I was able to get up and eat. It was worth it too. The chefs had whipped up a salad with lightly spiced lentils and homemade bread. Even Alice ate hers without a single complaint. I could see how chuffed Bea looked at this.

I was busy complimenting them when Bea smiled and told us that we hadn't seen anything yet. She cleared the table and got a bowl out from the fridge. 'I hear that

Charmaine's chocolate mousse is to die for. I'm not sure if my attempt will be quite up to standard, but let's try it and see.' She passed around bowls filled with the sweet dessert and the room was plunged into silence as we ate. I might have moaned out loud. I don't remember doing so but Jake was looking at me with lusty eyes. Poor guy, he'd have a few days wait before I'd be helping him out with that. No one had spoken yet when the quiet was broken by the sound of the phone ringing. Bea got up to answer it.

There wasn't any screaming or shouting, so we had no clues as to why she came back, opened a bottle of wine, poured and drank a whole glass before she sat back down again. Alice must have sensed something was up, because she climbed down from her chair and went to sit on her mum's knee. Bea snuggled her and kissed her hair. 'That was Daddy on the phone,' she said. Jake got up and grabbed himself a glass of wine. Charmaine and I sat there and didn't say a word. 'He was saying that he really misses you. Would you like him to come and pick you up and take you out somewhere nice tomorrow?'

Alice nodded and I saw Bea's eyes fill with tears. 'I thought you would. He'll come after breakfast and pick you up.' Alice got up and started dancing round the house cheering with excitement. Jake offered to go and look after her but Bea stopped him. 'She's going to be away from me all day tomorrow. I need to be with her now,' she said.

Charmaine and Jake cleared up while Bea put Alice in the bath. I offered to help but Jake was still feeling chivalrous and wouldn't let me. Charmaine left after the washing up was done, but even as Jake and I curled up on the sofa to watch some mindless TV, Bea still hadn't come downstairs. Jake checked on her when we went to bed and found that she'd gone to sleep cuddling Alice. We didn't wake her.

'It must be hell on her,' I said as we climbed into bed. 'She's the one who had to start over, make a home for her and Alice. Now he just rings up and gets to take Alice out and do the fun bits.'

'I know,' Jake said. Normally in bed he would wrap his arms around me and hold me close, but I could see how angry he was at his ex-brother-in-law. He was lying there stiffly. 'We actually used to be pretty close, Ted and me,' he said finally. I wasn't surprised by this, Bea had mentioned it once before, but Jake had never brought it up so I tried to give him the space to tell me himself. I could see how fond Jake was of his sister and it was clear that his niece meant the world to him. He continued, 'I was so angry when Ted left her. They had been together since they were sixteen. None of us saw it coming. Honestly, I don't know how Bea didn't throttle him.'

I drew Jake against me, and held him until I felt his body begin to relax. 'Bea is so lucky to have you,' I told him.

'And I'm lucky to have you,' he said, burying his face in my hair. 'I had pretty much stopped believing in love until I met you.' We fell asleep like that, and waking up felt even more intimate, to not be making love with our bodies, but to be to edging ever closer to saying the words to each other.

The following morning, Bea got Alice dressed and made her breakfast. Jake and I tried to stay out of the way until after Ted had been and gone. Afterwards Jake held Bea in his arms while she cried, then I made her tea and we took it in turns trying to offer her activities for the day but nothing we could think up was enough to distract her. 'I just need to get used to this,' she told us. 'Ted is her dad and it is good for her to have a relationship with him.' I thought she was being far more mature than I could have managed, until she added, 'Even though I wish he'd go down with a nasty case of bright blue boils all over his arse,' and to be fair, even then I couldn't blame her.

Eventually Bea dug out her old trainers and went for a jog. She said being active might distract her from being so angry. When she came back she was tired and her eyes looked like she'd been crying, so I wasn't sure how effective her plan had been. She spent the rest of the afternoon in her room. Ted had promised to bring Alice back by four, and at ten to four Bea came back downstairs and started pacing the hall. Jake offered to fetch her a drink, but she said that she didn't want Ted to smell it on her and have any grounds to criticise. I saw Jake puff himself up, as if he were a wild animal trying to make himself bigger to scare off a predator. I was glad he was feeling protective of his sister, but I wasn't sure what he would be able to do.

At five to four, when Bea had almost worn a hole in the carpet, the doorbell rang and Alice was stood there, beaming, with the biggest bunch of flowers I've ever seen. 'For you,' she said proudly, handing them to her mum. Bea's face lit up, even as she started crying.

'Sorry,' said the man who I presumed must be Ted, standing on the doorstep and waiting in vain to be invited inside. 'She wanted to choose something nice for you. I didn't mean to upset you. Not any more than I did already.' He looked at his shoes. 'I hope we were on time, we tried to be so that you weren't worried. I wanted to send you a few photos earlier so you'd know she was okay, but I didn't want to interrupt your day off.' He looked so sheepish that Bea finally took pity on him and let him in. She gestured towards the kitchen and started to make the tea. Jake growled behind me.

'Down, boy,' I told him.

'He'd better not try and weasel his way back in here,' he muttered.

'I think he knows he's blown it,' I said. 'Just trust Bea. She might need this.' I rested my hand on his arm as we followed them through, to try and help him to stay calm. In lieu of Jake saying anything I introduced myself. Ted shook my hand briefly, but his felt limp. It was a sure sign of how nervous he was.

'You've got a beautiful place here,' Ted said. I imagined all the retorts that were probably shooting through Jake's head, including 'no thanks to you' and 'I hope you don't think you'll be moving in here too'. I was glad for Bea's sake that he managed to stay quiet. Bea was perfectly capable of telling Ted what a fool he'd been by herself.

Alice dragged him up to see her room. As soon as he was out of earshot Bea took a deep breath and blew it out slowly.

'Are you okay?' I asked her.

She shook her head. 'Not really,' she admitted. 'I'm angry and hurt, but I'm also glad for Alice that she's getting to see her dad. I know she has missed him the last few months. She'd almost stopped asking for him, and I never meant for that to happen.'

She opened the fridge and started making Alice's tea, as if on autopilot. Ted came back downstairs by himself. He stepped towards Bea and asked for her help. 'Alice asked me to stay and read her a bedtime story, but I already told her that I can't. She's crying on her bed. I tried to explain that it's my fault, not hers, that I hadn't been doing a good job of being a daddy but I'm trying to learn. I'm sorry. I didn't mean to upset her.'

I think she must have realised how devastated he was, because instead of lashing out at him, she gave his arm a quick squeeze and went up to comfort their daughter. Ted just stood there, staring at the piles of pasta and cheese on the counter and shook his head.

'I don't even know what she likes for tea any more,' he muttered.

Even Jake eventually softened in the face of Ted's obvious sadness. 'Why don't you go back up with Bea?' he suggested. 'Maybe you can talk to Alice together.'

Ted ended up staying for tea, bathing Alice and reading to her until she fell asleep. Jake and I tried to stay out of their way, but I knew Jake wanted to be there and not at my flat so that he could make sure his sister was all right afterwards. Eventually Bea and Ted came back downstairs, and Bea led him into the kitchen. They called out to offer us a cup of tea, but we decided not to join them. Jake was muttering under his breath again. I knew he didn't want to risk seeing Bea get hurt, but she looked pretty relaxed, so we waited to hear what she would tell us afterwards.

Eventually Ted left, and Bea brought in a bottle of wine, three glasses and sat next to us on the sofa.

'You're not getting back together with that prick are you?' Jake asked, before she had even sipped her drink.

'Not a chance,' she scoffed. 'I was with him for so long that when he left I had no idea how I was ever going to cope, but I did. No, I'm not going back there again.'

'You seemed pretty cosy,' Jake pointed out.

'Actually, he was apologising if you must know,' Bea said. She took a celebratory swig of her drink, set her glass down and ran her hands through her hair. She stretched out her arms and rolled her neck, it was almost as though she was letting go of six months' worth of tension. 'At first when you told us about your mission, Evie, I must admit I didn't really understand it. I wasn't sure what you could learn from looking up men that you hadn't seen in years, and I thought it could only stir up unpleasant memories.'

'I just didn't want any of them to realise what they were

missing out on and try again,' Jake admitted, brushing a kiss against my ear.

'I get it now though,' Bea said, her eyes shining in the last of the summer sunshine that sneaked in through the window. 'I feel like I got some closure today,' she told us.

'I'm glad you said that. I was worried you were going to tell us you guys were going to try again,' Jake said to her.

'He hurt me too badly,' she said, shaking her head. 'And not just me. He walked away from Alice, and I'm not giving him the chance to hurt her twice. I was so angry when he left. I shouted and swore at him, but I was so pissed off I never stopped to listen to him.'

'Because there is no excuse for his behaviour,' scoffed Jake.

'He was wrong, he freely admitted that,' Bea explained. 'We'd been together so long that we never stopped to question whether we were actually good for each other any more. We were just starting to talk about having kids, and Ted asked if we could wait a while. A week later we found out we were already expecting,' she told us.

'I didn't know that,' Jake said.

'You don't exactly go round broadcasting it if your kid is an accident, or even just a welcome surprise,' Bea told him. 'Think how Alice would have felt if she found that out? Besides, we were married so it's not like anyone batted an eyelid when we told them our news.'

'I thought you were happy,' Jake said, sitting forward and staring at his sister. 'I'm sorry, I never knew that you were already having a hard time.'

She shrugged it off. 'We weren't at first,' she said. 'It was a surprise, but Ted was great. He came to all my doctor appointments, cried when we saw our first scan photo. He changed nappies, got up at night when she cried.'

'What happened?' I asked, wondering how their situation had broken down so irrevocably.

'It went downhill so slowly I barely noticed how bad it was until it was too late,' Bea said. 'The awful sleep slowly got to us, until we were snapping at each other constantly. If one of us slept better than the other, instead of being helpful and giving each other a rest, we grew resentful. Ted started to work longer hours so I was on my own with Alice more and more. Even when the sleep got better, we were already living separately, just within the same house. When the time came that he finally packed his bags, I was hurt but truthfully, I wasn't that surprised.'

'I didn't know,' Jake said again.

'What could you have done anyway?' Bea asked him. 'I was living it and I couldn't fix it. Tonight was the first time in years that we actually sat down calmly and talked about it. Ted apologised for leaving. As hard as it was when he went, I'm actually so much happier now I'm not living with all that stress. When he said sorry, I could finally let go of the anger.'

'That sounds really healthy,' I said.

'It feels it,' she replied. 'I can really understand why you wanted to go back to look at your past relationships. It felt so healing to let go of the pain.'

I thought about that but didn't point out that some of my experiences would hardly qualify to be called relationships. I certainly didn't want to go into too much detail about my past in front of Jake any more. Also, it hadn't exactly been closure that I'd been seeking. It was more a sense of remembering how I'd felt in the past.

Seeing Andy, Bill and Nick had been interesting. I'd remembered how it had felt to explore my femininity for the first time, but they hadn't had a huge impact on how I felt about myself. Not in the long term, anyway. They had allowed me to test out how it felt to be attracted to people, and any impact on my self-confidence from it not working out had been purely temporary. I'd bounced back from each setback fairly quickly, as teenagers generally do, compared to how long it had taken me to recover from Ryan. No, the real damage had come later.

Chatting with Rob and Jem had reassured me that they hadn't held any grudges, and that I hadn't upset anyone else so badly that I'd messed up their chances at happiness, especially given how settled Jem was now. It had been reassuring to remember that I could fall for guys who were actually nice people. Being with Rob had shown me that I could find someone who cared about me, and if I did, I shouldn't run from it. Jem had shown me that being with a partner could open up a new world of interests and experiences. I'd learnt more about theatre and art than I ever had before. We just hadn't had enough in common to keep us together, interest wise or temperament. But that was okay too. I'd felt so brave, getting to know them both, opening up emotionally and physically with them.

A lot of that confidence had come from George. The main lesson he had tried to impart was that I should be secure in myself, because of who I was. That was why he had been drawn to me again and again, and not because we had any formal ties to each other. Because we'd been friends too. I could learn from relationships, but I shouldn't define myself by them. And I had. I'd let Ryan chip away at me until I had doubted everything that made me who I was. I'd turned down promotions, and nearly missed out on being with Jake because I wasn't sure that I was good enough.

By going on my mission I had hoped to rebuild my self-confidence. Spending time with my brave, beautiful and bold cousin had helped. Seeing, and trusting, how Jake cared about me was a balm to my injured soul. He found me attractive, which was nice, but he wanted to spend time with me too, talking and just existing together, and not just for the sex. How he'd looked after me when I had period pains had proven that.

Seeing George at his wedding had reassured me that he wasn't the one who had got away, and that I'd benefited from having him in my life, even though I had lost sight of that for a while. He was so entranced by Zoe, and I'd certainly had fun with Jake at the hotel. It was time to let go of the pain from my past.

'So are you going to look up anyone else?' Bea asked me.

Jake didn't say anything, just sat back to watch how I responded. 'I don't need to,' I told them both. 'I'm so happy now, I don't think there is anything else I can learn from looking backwards any more.'

Jake seemed pleased to hear it and pulled me in for another squeeze. It felt good to let go. There had only really been one last person to look up, my ex-fiancé, and I didn't want to consider how relieved I felt at the idea of not getting back in touch with him. I'd always known that if I'd carried on with my challenge, that I'd get to him eventually, but the truth is I'd put off thinking about it for as long as I could. As it turned out, I didn't need to look Ryan up. The police found me first.

Chapter Twenty-Seven

It was never going to be a normal day. Jake's job searching had finally landed him an interview with a firm of graphic designers he told me were famous in their field. He seemed so excited to have the opportunity to work with them. It was just a shame that it was a two-hour train journey away. As much as I wanted it to go well for him, I had cried at the thought of no longer having him round the corner, though my tears were private, shed in the solitude of the bathroom because I didn't want to be the factor which stopped him going for a job that he really wanted. I wondered how I'd manage to sleep if he wasn't there holding me every night. I didn't tell him that either. We were still dancing around making declarations of our true feelings to each other, though we showed it in our actions freely enough. I didn't want to hold him back if this job was what he wanted, so on the morning of his interview I helped him try on several outfits until we found one that would fit well enough over his plaster cast.

I walked up to the station with him, talking up his CV and qualifications for the job, trying to boost his confidence even as my heart cracked more with every sentence. Kissing him goodbye before he descended the stairs to the platform, I managed to keep my tears in check until he was out of sight. This being London, no one stopped to ask me if I was okay, and I was grateful because I didn't know what I would have told them.

I managed to get my crying under control by the time I reached the café at the top of the high street. Inside I still felt like a quivering mess, but at least I wasn't openly bawling any more. I treated myself to a hot chocolate and a pastry, and sat staring out of the window, wondering how I would occupy myself so that I didn't spend the entire day climbing the walls, waiting to hear from Jake.

Bea had the day off so she had taken Alice to the zoo. She had been feeling guilty about working such long hours over the summer and was sad that she had missed out on the trips that Jake and I had taken Alice on. I think she had been even more excited than her daughter as they had got ready that morning. I therefore had the choice of sitting on my own in Jake's house or in mine. At least in my house I had more of my own junk to distract me from the waiting.

There were only two weeks remaining of the holiday, and I did need to start planning my lessons for the upcoming year. When Jake got back from his interview I would need to tell him that I wouldn't be able to help all day any more anyway. I'd allowed myself to have a real break the last few weeks, and to forget that school even existed, but I'd need to put in several hours every day between now and September to be ready in time. Real life was starting to creep into the bubble of contentment that I'd lived in all summer, and I wasn't happy or ready to let go of it.

It was hard to concentrate so I fell back on the techniques I'd used to get me through writing my dissertation at university. I set myself small targets, ten minutes of work at first then a reward of a cup of tea. Fifteen minutes and then a biscuit. Pretty soon I'd worked for a couple of hours and had almost managed to forget that Jake was currently pitching for a job that would take him far away if he got it. If only the ache in the pit of my stomach would go away.

Throwing my book across my bed, I found myself crying again. I wondered whether I should have told Jake how I felt before he'd left. Would he still have gone for the interview? If he hadn't, would he have resented me for holding him back? I'd never want to do that. So instead I crushed my pillow against my chest and fell asleep.

Waking up feeling groggy after a daytime nap that I hadn't really needed, I made a cup of coffee and tried to pull myself together. I checked my mobile but there were no messages. I went for a jog, pushing myself until I returned home nauseous and sweaty. I showered and tried to pick my work up again. Picking up my iPod, I skipped through the albums until I found something loud and powerful enough to drown out my own emotions. I managed to work for a few more hours, but it was slow going, trying to drag my restless brain to do my bidding. The tasks would have taken half the time with any decent levels of concentration.

Giving up, I picked up a light jacket and walked round to see if Bea and Alice were back from their day trip. As I knocked on their door, I realised that if they were still out I had no idea at all of what I would do with myself. Thankfully Bea answered the door. She took one look at me and pulled me in for a hug. I immediately burst into tears again.

She switched the TV on for Alice and led me through to the kitchen. She handed me a cup of sweet tea and a tissue and waited until I got myself back under control.

'I take it you aren't excited about Jake's job interview?' she asked me.

'I'm trying to be,' I told her. 'I just want what's best for him.'

'And what do you think that is?' she asked me.

I shook my head. 'I don't know,' I said. 'He's been job-hunting for a while. I think he was thrilled to finally get an interview. It's just, it's just …'

'That you wish this one wasn't so far away?' Bea added, in a quiet, gentle voice.

I found my eyes watering again and tried to blink the

tears away. 'I don't want to be selfish. If this job makes him happy ...' I began again.

'But you love him and you don't want to be away from him,' she continued.

I nodded. 'I haven't even told him how I feel yet. I didn't want to put any pressure on him either way. But I haven't heard from him all day and it's killing me.'

'I haven't heard anything either,' Bea said. 'I'd have called you if I had. But you need to relax. Trust Jake to make the right decision. It's obvious that he loves you too.'

'Do you think so?' I asked, desperately hoping that she was telling the truth.

'I know it, even if he doesn't yet. Give him time, Evie. We didn't have a model of a healthy adult relationship when we were growing up and I think seeing me and Ted split up threw him for a while too. But I've never seen him as happy and settled as he's been with you.'

'I don't want to lose him,' I told Bea, looking up at her with my bloodshot eyes. 'I've had my own demons to face to get to this point too. I finally feel ready to commit to him. I don't want it to be too late.'

'It won't be,' Bea said, putting her arm around me and giving me a squeeze. 'Come on, let's go and curl up with Alice and watch a film. We've walked so much today I think she's earned it, if she can stop pretending to be an elephant long enough to sit and watch it.'

Bea picked up the remote control and started to press buttons to switch the DVD player on. The local news flashed on, and the newsreader read out the first headline. A woman was in hospital following an attack in a local bar. Bea muted the sound as quickly as she could and tried to find the right channel for the movie.

Luckily Alice was oblivious, dancing round the room acting out the animals that she'd seen that day. Her impression of a penguin was cute and I found myself cheering up despite the butterflies in my stomach. The film was fun, Alice squealed at the monsters and hid her face against me, but seemed to enjoy it, especially when her mum brought the popcorn in. I found myself checking my mobile every two minutes, and though Bea saw what I was doing, she didn't say anything.

By seven o'clock I was all out of patience. 'He must know something by now,' I said, pacing the room. 'It couldn't possibly take this long to interview, what is he playing at? He must know we're waiting to hear.'

I started muttering about what I'd do to him when he got home, and Bea steered Alice out of the room and took her up for her bath. My phone rang and I jumped out of my skin. Noticing that the screen read 'private number', I rejected it wanting to keep the line clear for Jake to ring. As soon as I'd done that, I panicked in case Jake had used a different phone to ring me for any reason. I had tried not to call him all day because I hadn't wanted to interrupt, but now I couldn't wait any longer. I dialled his mobile and waited while it rang.

By the time it got to the fourth ring I was cursing under my breath. I was just about to hang up when Jake answered.

'Hi, hon, how did you get on?' I asked him.

'It was good,' he replied, amidst a background of crackling. 'I think they liked me.' He started to describe how well the interview had gone but the line started to break up. I heard 'answered questions well' and something about salary before the call dropped out completely. I tried to call back but it wouldn't connect at all. I went upstairs and told Bea the few words that I had heard. She counselled me not to give up on Jake already. I nodded but couldn't put together a reply. I let myself out and walked home.

Chapter Twenty-Eight

I kicked my sandals off, grabbed a bottle of lager from the fridge and switched my TV on. I thought I'd try Bea's trick of distracting myself with a movie, but for once even James Bond couldn't put a smile on my face. I figured that Jake had probably had such a bad connection because he had been on a train. Allowing a couple of hours for the journey, then another hour to make his way across London, even longer if he went to his house first to look for me, it might be late before he made it back.

I'd resigned myself to a restless evening waiting for him, and so jumped out of my skin when the doorbell rang ten minutes later. Wondering whether it might be Jake after all, I buzzed the downstairs door open without checking. It took my breath away when I opened my flat door and saw two police officers in uniform looking at me.

'Tell me it isn't Jake?' I said, stumbling back into the room until I fell onto the sofa. I felt my pulse rate spiking and my breathing growing jagged. 'Don't let Matt have finally got himself into trouble.'

The officers looked at each other. The male officer was in his early thirties, with brown almond eyes and a police badge fixed to his turban. He held his hands up to calm me down, and his gentle voice was soothing to my nerves. 'Don't worry,' he assured me. 'These Jake and Matt fellows are fine, as far as we know. That's not why we're here.' They introduced themselves but I instantly forgot their names. My mind was too hung up worrying why they were there.

I got my emotions back under control and offered them a cup of tea. I knew I was stalling for time before I found out what had brought them here, but I was in no rush now that I knew my boys were safe. The male officer turned down my offer of tea, but the female officer accepted. She suggested that we both have some, and so I returned shortly with two cups. Sitting down I tried to guess what they might be there for but couldn't.

'You might have heard on the local news tonight that a lady was found in a critical condition following an incident at a bar last night,' she began.

My hands flew to my mouth and I started trying to remember whether my cousin had told me if she was working or going out the night before. 'It wasn't Charmaine, was it?' I asked, feeling selfish that I hadn't asked about her when I'd asked about Matt and Jake.

'No,' said the man, and I immediately found myself able to breathe again. 'It's Tina Clark, though we haven't released her name to the press yet.'

I clattered my cup back on to the coffee table, not caring that half the contents spilled over the side. I fled to the bathroom and barely got the lid of the loo open before I threw up. The lady officer came into the bathroom and waited quietly until I'd stopped heaving. She offered me a glass of water, and didn't speak any more until after I'd brushed my teeth and rinsed my face.

'She woke up this afternoon and she's been asking for you,' the man said as I returned to the room. 'We've arrested her partner, a Mr Ryan Stapleford. Tina told us that you were previously engaged to Mr Stapleford and the investigating officers wondered whether you might be able to provide some useful background information.'

I nodded and began to gather up my handbag and a jacket. I reached for my car keys but the lady officer stopped me. 'Don't worry, we'll drive you,' she told me. 'We'll go to the station first. The boss is waiting for you there. Then we can go on to visit Tina afterwards.'

That was fine by me, I was in no rush to see her again. I didn't stop to consider why I felt so strongly, even now that she was injured. Hell, especially now that she was injured. They led me outside to their car, and I found myself for the first time in my life sat in the back of a police car. That was almost enough to distract me from the disquiet I felt inside.

Pulling up outside the police station, the woman police officer got out and escorted me through various doors and corridors. She swiped us through several security doors, and I was relieved to think she'd have to do the same to get us out again and that I wouldn't have to find my own way. My head was spinning and I had no idea how many left and right turns we'd just taken.

Opening one final door, she ushered me into an interview room and left me alone while she went to fetch yet more tea. It was lighter inside than I'd expected, and I was relieved to see that there were no bars on the window in here. I wanted to tell her that I couldn't drink another drop but she'd already gone. There was a light tap at the door, and a plain-clothes officer let himself in.

Sitting at the opposite side of the desk, he uncapped a pen and opened a file. There were photos of Tina lying in hospital. There was a close up of a wound on the back of her head. He quickly gathered them up and hid them underneath another piece of paper. I wondered whether he'd deliberately spilled them, then considered why he might have done that. To scare me? To ensure I understood the seriousness of why we were there? I was under no doubt of that already.

The lady who had picked me up at the flat returned, placed a cup of tea in front of me and left without another word. The investigating officer, a man in his late forties with greying hair and greying eyes, watched me, and I found myself picking it up and drinking just to have something to do with my hands. 'I'm DI Spencer,' he said, as he stared. His dark suit was rumpled, his tie knot pulled loose, and I wondered how many hours he'd been working already.

'We responded to a 999 call from a bar in town last night and arrived to find the victim unconscious,' he began.

I tried to take another sip of tea but my hands were shaking so badly I couldn't do it.

'Officers on the scene arrested a man, a Mr Stapleford of Swindon Close, and have charged him. I don't need to tell you how serious this is. From what we've pieced together, he struck Miss Clark, which caused the victim to fall backwards and hit her head on the corner of a glass table. The victim had surgery overnight due to the head wound. Upon regaining consciousness this morning, she was heard asking for you repeatedly. The question is, why? I've reviewed the CCTV from last night and having seen you now I know you weren't present. So why was my victim asking for you instead of telling us about the bastard who hurt her?'

Whilst I was surprised to hear an officer describe Ryan as a bastard, he was correct in the description. I took a deep breath and wondered where to begin with this story, the last in my notebook and the one I hadn't yet even told Jake about.

'Tina and I were best friends growing up,' I began. DI Spencer nodded and I continued. 'I met Ryan almost three years ago. We dated for a year before getting engaged. We broke up six months later and he began dating Tina. I haven't seen or spoken to either of them since.'

DI Spencer scribbled some notes on his notepad. His approach softened as he continued, 'Why do you think Tina asked for you? Needless to say, these are serious charges.'

'She probably knew that if she asked for me after this, I'd be there. We haven't spoken since she started seeing Ryan, but I wasn't waiting for something like this to happen before I made peace. Bloody hell.' I rubbed my eyes with my hands then looked up at the detective. 'More likely though, she wanted me to make sure that I came forward and told you that, yes, Ryan could absolutely have meant to hurt her.'

Chapter Twenty-Nine

The interview continued for another half hour, but after I'd answered the same questions three times I was ready to go. I suspected that they were trying to find a way to get evidence of Ryan's intent to harm Tina, or were trying to find out if his violent behaviour was part of a pattern, but I wasn't sure how telling them about my experiences could help. They had been interested to hear about how unpleasant Ryan had been, but I couldn't tell them anything about his violent outburst. He had been horrible to me, but he hadn't raised a fist. Had I been lucky, or was there a more sinister reason? They didn't, or couldn't, tell me. Finally, I stood up and asked whether I could visit my friend now. A new officer arrived and drove me to the General. Visiting hours were over, but going in with a uniformed officer encouraged the nurses to waive any complaints. The officer led me to the ward, pointed in the direction of Tina's bed and disappeared.

Tina was asleep, and I didn't want to wake her. She looked so delicate, her left eye swollen almost shut, black hair spread out on the pillow. The rest of her face was pale from blood loss and pinched in pain, even in her sleep. I took her hand and rested my forehead on her bed. I woke up to find her gently squeezing my fingers.

'Oh, Tina,' I said, stroking her hand. It was about the only part of her that didn't look hurt and wasn't covered in blankets or wires.

'I'm sorry,' she said.

'What do you have to be sorry for?'

'It's all my fault,' she said.

'None of this is your fault. You didn't ask for this.' I

could have pointed out to her that Ryan had caused all the pain here but I couldn't bring myself to utter his name.

'How do I look?' she asked. I smiled, a year without seeing her and she hadn't changed.

'Like shit,' I told her. I wasn't angry at her any more. How could I be with her lying here? Still, I didn't find myself able to be anything other than blunt.

'You never could hide your emotions, Red, could you?' she pointed out. 'I asked for a mirror but they won't bring me one.'

'Maybe you don't want to see,' I told her.

'I need to,' she told me, gripping my hand even tighter. 'This was the last time he gets to lay a finger on me. I need to know how bad it is, so that I never go back.'

Without another word I got my phone from my pocket. It had been turned off since I got in the police car, and I switched it back on and selected the camera app. Taking a few photos, I showed them to Tina. She winced when she saw her face.

My phone buzzed and I took it back to find a string of text messages and voicemails. 'I need to make a quick call,' I told Tina. She told me to go to the bathroom to make sure that none of the nurses saw me on a mobile and asked me to leave. I did as she suggested and found myself calling Jake back from a dingy little bog that smelt strongly of pee.

'Evie, where the hell are you?' he said when he picked up. 'I looked everywhere for you. I wanted to tell you about the job.'

I swore under my breath, assuming this meant that he got it, but I couldn't begin to think of that now. 'I'm at the hospital,' I told him.

He went quiet for a moment. 'Which one?' he asked. 'I'm on my way. I'll call a cab and be there in ten minutes.'

'The General,' I told him. 'But there's no rush. I'm not injured. Hurt, but not injured.'

He sounded confused, but promised to come anyway. I told him which ward we were in, and hung up. Returning to Tina's bed I picked up her hand again.

'What the hell happened, Tina?' I asked her.

'He thought I was chatting to another guy in the bar. He punched me in the face, though it was the table which caused most of the damage.' She laughed but there was no humour in it. 'I'd only been asking where he got his jacket because Ryan mentioned that he liked it and I wanted to get him one for his birthday,' she said.

'Was this the first time he hit you?' I asked, reading the answer from her body language even as I asked it. Tina shook her head. 'Oh, Tina,' I said again, as I held her hand. I wanted to hug her properly but I didn't dare for fear of hurting her. 'I spoke to the police,' I told her.

'They were here earlier too,' Tina replied. 'I wasn't in much of a state to talk though. They said they'd be back tomorrow.' She tried to sit up but winced as she moved. I offered to call a nurse but she waved me to sit down again. 'I've had as many painkillers as they'll give me already,' she said, through a grimace of pain. 'Besides, every time it hurts I get more determined to see the son of a bitch behind bars for this.'

'I'll back you every step of the way,' I promised. She squeezed my hand again, and though I was devastated to see her in this condition, I also felt like I had regained my friend. We heard a commotion at the entrance to the ward and I turned to see Jake arguing with a nurse. I leant over, kissed Tina's cheek and told her I'd be back to see her the next day.

I picked my handbag up from the floor and walked out to Jake. He had taken his tie off but still wore the shirt we'd picked out that morning. I could barely believe now that it was the same day, so much seemed to have happened since I'd last seen him. He held me at arm's length and looked me up and down as if reassuring himself that I wasn't injured. I reassured him that my hurt wasn't a physical one, then threw myself into his arms. He held me and kissed me.

We walked out through the same exit I'd left only weeks earlier after Jake's accident. The sounds were similar, sirens in the distance, a low level of conversation, taxi engines as people were dropped off or picked up. The smells were familiar too; disinfectant, boiled food, and an underlying current of exhaust fumes. My emotions last time I'd left had been a jumble, I'd been so relieved that he was going to be okay, excited at our kiss and yet nervous about what it might mean. This time I was so overwhelmed my brain had shutdown and I couldn't have put together a meaningful thought if I'd tried.

Jake seemed to sense that I needed him. He led me to a taxi that was waiting at the cab rank, got in next to me and helped click my seat belt into place. He held my hand all the way home, speaking only to ask whether I wanted to go back to his house or mine. I needed the security of my own space, and the reminder of my independence that my flat provided, so we went back there.

Jake paid for the taxi. I wanted to contribute but could hardly fumble in my bag to find my purse, let alone dig out the change to pay. Jake took my key from me and let me in. He placed his good arm around me and I leant on him as we walked in and up the stairs. He sat me on the sofa, fetched me a glass of wine from the kitchen and covered me with a blanket. I sat and stared at the wall as he moved.

'Do you want to tell me about it?' he asked. I shook my head. 'You look like you need to sleep, Evie. Come on, I'll help you into bed and leave you in peace. I'll come back in the morning so we can talk.'

My eyes flew open and I spoke my first sentence in an hour. 'Don't leave me. Please don't go, Jake, I need you to hold me.'

I woke up to find myself wrapped around Jake. My hair lay against his chest and he was awake, stroking it and watching me. I drew the sheet up over our naked bodies, and I remembered asking Jake to make love to me in the middle of the night. His soft movements had finally chased the demons from my mind and allowed me a few hours of sleep.

'Good morning, sleeping beauty,' he said, kissing me again.

'Thank you,' I told him, squeezing myself even tighter against his chest.

'Are you ready to talk?' he asked. 'You don't need to tell me if you don't want to, but, Evie, I've never seen you so scared.'

I got up and pulled a T-shirt over my head. I found some old jogging bottoms and went into the kitchen to make coffee. Jake followed me. He had paused to pull on his boxer shorts, but otherwise he was naked but for the plaster cast on his wrist. I made our drinks and we took them to the sofa. I pulled Jake's good arm around me and sat with my back pressed against his chest so that he couldn't see my face as I spoke.

I began by telling Jake why I had really begun revisiting my past in the first place. The wedding invitation had acted as a trigger, but even before that arrived I'd realised that being with Ryan had stripped away so much of my belief in myself. I'd lost the confidence that I'd slowly built up from my experiences with George and Jem. I told Jake that I'd been trying to go back in time to a place where I felt good about myself again.

Meeting up with my exes, the first two experiences aside, had proved to me that despite how things had ended with Rob and Jem, I hadn't been wrong to choose them. Getting back in touch had shown me what sweet guys they were. Even seeing George so happy with Zoe had been healing. He had never lied to me; he'd been so gentle, letting me take the lead. He'd provided a safe place for me to experiment, and any hurt I'd felt that he didn't reciprocate my feelings wasn't really his fault. He'd never misled me into thinking he felt the same way. I'd done that for myself. He had only ever tried to boost my confidence so that one day I would meet someone who thought I was special. It had just taken me a long time to realise that he had never been talking about himself.

It was reassuring to realise that some amount of dating and breaking up was normal. It had helped me to find out who I was, what I wanted in a relationship, and how I should and shouldn't behave in order to make it work. Remembering how it felt to be desired, I could see why Charmaine enjoyed dressing well. It felt powerful.

Meeting Jake had been the icing on the cake. He made me feel beautiful, and cared for, and had removed the last of the insecurities I'd held onto. I told him about the police turning up on my doorstep and how scared I'd been at the thought that something had happened to him. I talked about my meeting at the police station, and how it had felt to see Tina for the first time in months, injured and alone in a hospital bed.

I cried as I spoke, and he held me and rocked me. I continued on, telling him that Ryan had been the last man in my little black book. I had decided since meeting Jake that I didn't need to look back any more, and I'd been relieved not to think about Ryan again. Finally I admitted how nervous I had become, those last few weeks that we'd been engaged. He had never laid a finger on me, but when the police told me what he'd done to Tina, I'd believed them instantly. It shook me to think that at one time I'd planned to spend the rest of my life with the monster.

Jake listened quietly, handing me tissues as I cried and rubbing my back when he sensed that I needed comforting. When I finished talking, he turned me round so that he could look me in the eye. He kissed away the last of my tears, and spoke slowly, as if trying to make sure I hung on his every word.

'This wasn't your fault, Evie,' he told me again. 'You couldn't have known how violent he would be to your friend. And what kind of friend goes out with your ex-fiancé so soon after you break up anyway?'

'She didn't deserve to end up in hospital,' I reminded him.

'I never for a moment thought that she did,' he assured me. 'I just want you to see the bigger picture. There were obviously things going on that you didn't know anything about.' He ran his hands through his hair, pushing his fringe away from his eyes. 'I'm just glad that you dumped the fucker before he injured you,' he said, leaning over to kiss me.

I pulled back, out of his reach. 'That's the thing,' I said. 'I didn't dump him. He broke up with me.'

Chapter Thirty

Jake was quiet, and I wondered what he thought of me now that he knew. I wasn't the strong person he'd assumed I was. I hadn't walked away when things had got tough. I'd wanted to, and I liked to tell myself that I would have, and that it would have been sooner rather than later. I hoped that if it had been up to me I'd still have escaped from Ryan before he'd injured me as badly as he'd hurt my friend. I couldn't guarantee that I would have though.

Eventually I got up and made some breakfast, more to keep busy than because I had any kind of appetite. Handing Jake a plate of toast, I sat down next to him again and tried to force myself to eat something.

'I don't understand,' Jake said, finally breaking the silence. 'Why didn't you leave him?'

'Because he'd been so sweet when we first got together,' I said. 'Then as he slowly changed, there was never one thing that happened that was bad enough to make me walk away. At the time I thought that it would either get back to how it had been at the start soon or I would think about leaving him. The shitty stuff just crept in. One day his magazines had to be lined up neatly. That was fine. It's nice to be tidy. Then he started to complain about my books. They took up too much space. I think he hated when I bought a new one as I'd have long baths and read them cover to cover. I wasn't there to run around after him. A few weeks later I came home and he'd thrown my books out, saying they were crap and that I only read them because I wasn't bright enough to read proper literature. I was so shocked I couldn't even begin to point out that I'd read English Lit at uni. Then he came home the next day and apologised. He said he'd been stressed at work, and he bought me a new hardback that I'd been wanting.' I couldn't begin to explain to Jake how the constant corrections of my behaviour or my speech or my actions had worked to slowly erode my confidence until I had actually started to doubt my own abilities.

'So you thought he'd change each time, but he didn't?' Jake asked.

I shook my head. 'I never managed to rebuild the collection he got rid of. I didn't get the chance because he came home one day and told me that he was breaking up with me. He gave me an hour to pack my bags, then he threw them out into the street. We'd been together for a year and a half and that was how he treated me. I didn't know what to do with myself. I had no idea where I'd stay. I didn't want to go home and explain to my parents what had happened so I went to see Tina.'

'Only to find out that she was seeing him. No wonder you were angry with her.'

I tried to eat another bite of toast but could hardly swallow. 'Now I'm kicking myself, wondering if I should have warned her, but, honestly, looking back, I don't know what I could have said that she'd have listened to.'

'So what did you do?' Jake asked me.

'I crashed at Charmaine's for a week, told my folks that Ryan and I had decided to break off our engagement, then found this flat and I've lived here ever since.'

'No wonder you're attached to the place, dodgy plumbing and all,' Jake said, trying to tease a smile out of me. 'It seems to me though that anyone who can go out with their friend's ex so quickly should know that the bloke is a wanker.'

I had to agree with him, and yet given that it was my friend lying in a hospital bed, put there by someone I'd once been engaged to, I couldn't shake the guilt. Maybe Tina should have known that Ryan wasn't a nice guy for dumping me for her, but she'd have had no way of knowing that this was only the top of his own personal iceberg of awfulness.

'I'm going to have a quick shower,' I said, giving up on my food. 'Visiting times start in an hour, I thought I'd go back and see Tina. She seemed determined not to go back to him yesterday. I want to make sure she still feels the same way now.'

Jake stood up as I did but didn't move to start getting dressed. He still seemed pensive, taking in what I'd told him about my past. I stopped to give him a kiss before I left. 'I know that this has probably shocked you,' I told him. 'It was one thing seeing me go back and relive my glory days at university; it's another finding out about this. I just wanted to thank you for being there for me last night. And for not running a mile when I told you the rest of it this morning.'

Jake pulled me into his arms and rested his chin on the top of my head. 'Evie, I could never run from you.' He tipped my chin with one finger so that I was looking up at him. 'I love you.'

'I love you too,' I said, relieved to finally say the words out loud. 'I think I have for a long time.'

'Since you came to visit me in hospital and were so happy to find me alive that you kissed me until my heart skipped a beat,' he said.

'Maybe,' I admitted. 'Or maybe since you burnt the cake.' He kissed me again. 'I'll call you when I get back from the hospital,' I told him.

I'd been out the door for ten minutes before I realised that I still hadn't asked how his job interview had gone.

* * *

Tina had been moved to a private room on the same ward, and as I opened the door I realised that she wasn't alone. I hadn't meant to interrupt, but she waved me in and pointed to the chair next to her bed. I dropped my bag on the floor underneath, shrugged off my cardigan and sat down. She was chatting to a woman, around our age, mid-to-late-twenties, with long curly blonde hair, which she wore in a messy ponytail. She was wearing jeans and a tight T-shirt with a picture of an old kids TV show on the front. She had earrings all the way up her ears, and so many silver studs in them I lost count. I wondered who she was. Clearly she wasn't a police officer.

Stepping into the room I saw a pile of leaflets on the bed. 'This is Steph,' Tina said, making the introductions. Steph and I stood up and did an awkward handshake. Neither of us was completely comfortable with meeting over the bed of an injured lady without knowing why the other person was there. 'I found a telephone helpline number on the back of the loo door when I went to the bathroom and gave them a ring. Steph kindly agreed to come and visit me. I needed to talk to someone, face to face. She works with people who have, or had, violent partners. I thought I'd better see about getting some advice.'

'Apart from stay away from the bastard?' I asked.

Tina nodded. 'I intend to,' she assured me. 'Evie knows Ryan too,' she said to Steph by way of introducing me.

'Sadly, it isn't always as simple as planning to stay away,' Steph chipped in. Her voice gentle but assured. 'Sometimes partners apologise and women decide to give them another chance.'

'That's not going to happen here,' I growled. Tina shook her head too. I got the feeling Steph was supposed to be trying to stay neutral, but I could tell from the ghost of a smile that flitted across her face that she was pleased with Tina's vehemence.

'It can be very hard when you first leave; it's a big upheaval, moving house, feeling lonely. But try to remember why you made that decision to get yourself safe,' she continued.

'I'll have the scar to remind me too,' Tina pointed out, gingerly touching the back of her head.

'Do people really go back to their partners after they've been attacked?' I asked, thinking as soon as I said it that I'd put up with all kinds of crap and stayed so I wasn't one to talk.

'More frequently than you think, sadly,' Steph answered. 'It's different to being assaulted by a stranger. There are a lot more emotions involved, a history. Often there are children, the wife might be scared of bringing them up on her own, she might struggle for money. Sometimes he apologises, swears he won't do it again.'

'But he does,' I chipped in.

'All too often,' Steph agreed. 'Sometimes it can be like a cycle. You have the violent incident, then he's repentant, attentive, saying sorry, buying gifts, making all kinds of promises. But all too soon it shifts and he becomes slowly more aggressive, slowly more threatening, then eventually he is violent and the cycle starts all over again.'

'So some people get hurt like this over and over again?' I asked, gesturing to the bruise on Tina's face, which was now a vivid shade of purple.

Steph nodded again. 'I've talked to people on the helpline who have experienced abuse for decades.' Tina and I fell silent. 'That doesn't mean that you have to,' Steph continued, trying to reassure her. 'It is possible to leave and go on to live a perfectly normal happy life. This is your opportunity to decide what it is that you want to do.'

'Not being put in hospital would be a good start,' I muttered and Tina shot me a dirty look. 'Sorry,' I said, and sat down, taking her hand. 'I just can't believe it came to this.'

'That's a hard one too,' Steph continued. I got the feeling she enjoyed raising awareness and that this was a topic she cared about passionately. I could only imagine how forthright she would have been had she not been mindful of Tina's injury and emotions. She seemed to weigh her words carefully before she spoke again. 'Often the first violence doesn't occur until later in a relationship, after the couple are married, pregnant or have small children. That doesn't mean that the relationship was perfect to begin with, though I guess there is no such thing as completely perfect, but the abusive behaviours can start out fairly innocuous and get worse over time.'

'What do you mean?' I asked. She'd grabbed my attention now. I wondered if this could explain why my relationship with Ryan had gone downhill and how he had then progressed on to be violent with Tina.

'Often we find that violent partners display a range of other controlling behaviours,' Steph explained. 'In some cases they control the finances so that their partners have little or no financial freedom. They have to ask for money to buy anything or provide receipts. Other men go through the credit card bill with a fine-tooth comb. Being financially savvy is fine, sensible even, but it's about the power imbalance. One partner controlling the other, and this is just one arena where we see it.'

I sat back, thinking about how when Ryan and I had moved in together we'd set up a joint account for bills. He'd been pretty thorough with tracking what we'd spent. He'd claimed he was being responsible, but it had niggled me and so I'd kept my own account for the majority of my wages. Just before we split up he'd started asking, more and more forcefully, for me to pay my salary into the joint account. It was one of the few times that I'd stood up to him, and it was lucky that I had. I'd needed every penny I could access to pay for the deposit and first month's rent for my flat when he kicked me out. If he'd controlled all my money, I would have struggled to leave. Maybe this was one of the reasons he had been able to dominate Tina, she had no family or friends to run to.

'Other partners demand seemingly innocuous things around the house be a certain way, and it can creep in slowly, all these little rules that you realise you mustn't break or it gets unpleasant, but each one on their own isn't bad enough that you break up over it.' I thought about Ryan's insistence, which began shortly after we got engaged, that we cook proper meals at home. At the time he'd talked about how much healthier and cheaper it was to live this way, explaining that it would help us to save up for the wedding. Looking back he hadn't ever done any of the shopping or cooking, even though we both worked full time. It wasn't a factor that was difficult enough to cause a breakdown in our relationship, but it had affected his mood and put extra demands on me but few, if any, on him. He had been particular about which foods I cook and how his meals tasted. I'd had to leave work early many, many times to fit in an extra trip to the shop for an ingredient or two so that I could cook that evening's dinner exactly to Ryan's specification. A failure to do so could lead him to spending the rest of the evening sulking or complaining at me. I'd hoped that he would go back to how he had used to be soon, and told myself it was the stress of saving up or him having a bad day at work. Now I knew that it wasn't true. He'd behaved that way because he thought it was acceptable.

Steph's descriptions of violent and abusive partners explained why the police had been so interested to hear about my relationship with Ryan. It was evidence of a lot of the early controlling behaviours. I began to realise what a lucky escape I had had. It also explained why the police had been so interested to talk to me. They must have wondered whether I had been through similar experiences to Tina and never reported it. My experiences of being with him were also why I had found it so easy to understand that he had injured Tina. Though he hadn't hit me, somewhere in the primitive parts of my brain, that fear had been lurking. It was why I'd worked so hard to appease him and keep him calm. Underlying my behaviour was the knowledge that I wasn't really safe. I'd never wanted to admit, even to myself, that when he threw a mug against the wall and smashed it, or ripped up a magazine that I was reading because I'd been slow to get up and greet him when he got in from work, his underlying message hadn't been that he was doing that to save me from his temper, it had been showing me how easily he could have broken me instead. No wonder it had taken me so long to begin to heal after we'd split up.

Steph wasn't done yet though with her explanations. 'These behaviours might seem similar to those that take place within a "healthy" relationship.' She used her fingers to make an air quote around the word 'healthy'. 'But within an abusive relationship the acts have an undercurrent of power imbalances. They're not joint decisions, they're actions that are carried out in order to appease the abusive partner and avoid confrontations.'

I remembered the fight we'd had two weeks before Ryan dumped me. It was a Friday night and I'd had a long week at work as we'd had our school inspection. I had period pains and a thumping headache. I was too tired to cook so I'd picked up fish and chips and a veggie burger for me on the way home. I'd been hoping for a peaceful evening, a soak in the bath and some mindless TV. Instead Ryan had gone mad. He'd thrown the takeaway against the wall and shouted at me for wasting the food in the fridge. I'd ended up cleaning up, making us a quick soya mince spag bol and crying in the bath. I hadn't mentioned that he'd been the one to waste the takeaway.

The next day Ryan had been full of apologies. He said he'd had a busy week at work too. He took me out for dinner and promised that we could get a takeaway the following week. He'd chosen such a posh restaurant, one that I normally thought of as far too expensive and I'd felt thoroughly spoilt. I started to see how his behaviours fit into the models Steph was outlining. I noticed that Tina was nodding too, and I wondered what she'd been through over the last year. I realised that some of the after-effects of living with Ryan were still with me now. I was careful about what I spent but I never checked my bank balance. I rarely had more than a few items in my fridge, and I had takeaways at least once a week. Even after months of freedom I was still rebelling.

'And that's before you even consider the impact on other close relationships,' Steph continued. I snapped out of my reminiscences and tuned back in to what she was saying. 'It can be hard to maintain friendships. Lots of women stop inviting friends over because their houses have to be kept in a certain way, or because they never know what his mood will be like and they don't want their friends to realise what they're living with.'

I shook my head. Tina had been a frequent visitor to our flat before Ryan kicked me out, though obviously that hadn't ended well for any of us. Steph was still talking though. 'Other times, it is more subtle. The abusive partner belittles friends. He might be so rude or nasty about people that you stop talking about seeing them, then you see them less often. Eventually your other bonds weaken and you find yourself even more dependent on the man and with fewer options of who to talk to when it gets difficult.'

I found myself flashing back again to the times I'd gone out with Charmaine while I'd lived with Ryan. He'd been rude before she arrived, putting down her taste in clothes, calling her slutty though anyone else could see she'd looked gorgeous. I'd begun to meet her at her flat instead when we went out, but by the time Ryan had dumped me we hadn't been out together for a few months. No wonder she had been so relieved at the break up. I also realised how many of my hang-ups about what I wore stemmed from this. No wonder I'd felt a lot freer this summer as I started to wear dresses and little tops again. I hadn't realised how much impact Ryan had had on my behaviours.

I looked at Tina and wasn't surprised to see that she was crying. If I'd got myself so messed up I wondered how she was feeling. 'I'm so sorry, I should have come back and warned you about his moods,' I told her.

'How could you? We weren't exactly speaking, and that was my fault. Besides, Ryan would have been in my other ear, telling me it was jealousy, or that he'd never treat me like that. And he was convincing. Every time he said sorry. Every time he promised me that he had changed.'

I think Steph sensed that we were straying into territory Tina wasn't ready to go to yet. She reached out and gave Tina's hand a gentle pat. 'There's a lot of support out there though for women who are trying to move on. We've got a local helpline if you need to speak to someone. There's national helplines too, those run twenty-four hours a day. We can meet with you and offer you practical advice about moving on, or we can simply listen if you feel like you just need to talk about what happened. When it comes to the court case, we can make sure that you are fully supported throughout the process too.'

Tina's tears had slowed but not stopped. I reached into my handbag, juggling junk until I finally found a little pocket pack of tissues. Handing them to Tina and waiting until she'd wiped her eyes and blown her nose, I tucked a stray strand of hair behind her ear and tried to reassure her too.

'You hear that, you're not on your own. You've got all these experts backing you up, and you've got me too. I'm going to be right by your side from now on.' I didn't point out that the longer Steph had talked for, the more I'd realised that it could have been me lying in Tina's place so easily.

Chapter Thirty-One

Piles of books which needed reading and lessons that needed planning waited for me at my flat so when I left the hospital I went straight to Jake's house. He greeted me with a hug, and didn't seem to mind when I didn't let go of him. He guided me inside and sat me down on the sofa. Alice bounded in to greet me, and I tried to perk up and chat with her, but I found it really hard to concentrate on what she was saying. I think Jake could see me fading in and out. He set Alice up in the other room with her colouring book and pens, came back into the kitchen and offered me tea.

'You look like what you really need is a stiff drink, but given that it's not even lunchtime maybe you'd rather wait?' I nodded, and he continued. 'I'm not sure if you're agreeing with the tea or the stronger drink, so let's start with tea and see if that does the trick.'

'Thank you,' I said as he set the steaming mug down next to me.

'Do you want to talk about it?' he asked, his voice soft and gentle. He stepped back, leaning against the long wooden counter that ran the length of the room. Maybe he thought that I needed the space. I didn't. I wanted the safety of his arms but it was hard to find the words to tell him. My mind was a fog of memories, fears and confusion. Sipping my tea, I tried to think how to express the emotions and memories that the last few days had stirred up. I tried to speak, but my voice cracked and all that came out was more tears. He was there instantly, crushing me to his chest.

I felt his heartbeat, slow and steady against my cheek. Eventually I slowed my breathing and my tears. 'It could have been me,' I told him, looking up at his beautiful blue eyes. 'It could have been me lying in that hospital bed.'

'But it isn't,' he pointed out, as if that made it all better. As if it took away the fact that my friend was recovering from a beating.

'If he hadn't dumped me for my friend, who is to say I'd have left him in time?' I explained to Jake about the warning signs I'd missed, the controlling behaviours that I'd put up with.

He listened without speaking, and I wondered whether I was losing him as I spoke, whether he'd still want to be with me once he realised how weak I had been. I couldn't stop though. I told him about the fish and chip argument, and how, before I met him, I'd hadn't worn a dress in a year because of how much damage Ryan had done to my self-esteem.

By the time I finished I knew my skin would be as red as my hair, I wasn't a pretty crier. My nose was running and I was taking big, heaving gulps of air every few seconds to power the tears. Jake walked to the cupboard, opened it and handed me a huge bar of Dairy Milk. 'I'm sure Bea won't mind you raiding her stash,' he said. 'This seems like an emergency.'

I broke off a line of chocolate and started chewing. Jake motioned to his T-shirt. He had huge soggy patches where I'd been pressing against him. 'I might just go and grab a clean top,' he said. Alice walked in as he left the room.

'I bumped my knee,' she said, pointing at her leg. I leaned in closer but couldn't see any mark.

'I think you're okay,' I told her, wiping my eyes so that she wouldn't see the tears, but that was the wrong thing to say and she held her breath. 'Do you want a plaster?'

'Only Mummy kisses can make it better,' she said, thrusting her bottom lip out.

'Luckily I have a spare one of those in my pocket,' I told her. She looked sceptical, but I mimed looking in my pocket, finding an invisible kiss, holding it with my fingertips and applying it to her knee. She wasn't sure, but thankfully she was distracted when she noticed the chocolate. I handed her a couple of squares and she wandered off quite happily. If only adult upsets were solved so easily.

'Can I make you better with a kiss too?' Jake asked, standing in the doorway.

'I'd like you to try,' I told him. He leaned over and started with a gentle kiss, the merest brush of his lips against mine. I stood up and pressed myself against him and kissed him deeper and longer.

'Is it working?' he asked.

'You're healing me in places I hadn't realised were broken,' I told him. 'I'm so glad that you lived here instead of Billy Banks.'

Jake laughed. 'I take it you really are done with looking back into your past now?'

I nodded. 'I'm all about the future,' I told him. 'If you still want me?'

'Evie,' he said, stepping back. 'Why on earth wouldn't I?'

I shrugged. 'I'm damaged goods.'

'So am I,' he said, gesturing to his sling.

'For one more week,' I scoffed.

'You can't write yourself off just because you went out with a loser. Hell, I probably know more about the guys you dated than I wanted to, and I hate every one who put any doubt into your mind about how amazing you are.' He kissed me again. 'I love that you gave up your holidays to look after Alice and me just because we needed you. I love that you find kisses in your pocket to calm her down when she feels sad. I love that when you were hurting, instead of curling up into a ball and giving up, you came up with this crazy scheme to heal yourself and make it better. And it's working. Look at you, even in just the time I've known you you're so much more confident than you were.'

I stroked his face, running my fingers across his stubbly cheeks. 'How could I not be healed when I'm with you?' I asked. 'You're the super uncle, ready to burn cakes, tackle cars and rescue damsels in distress.'

'It isn't just because we're together,' he assured me. 'It's within you too. You say you wore baggy clothes? How about the girl I saw dancing in just a handkerchief in the club? We weren't together then but every guy in the place was staring at you, including me. I couldn't take my eyes off you.'

'You looked pretty hot yourself,' I pointed out.

'You say you stopped believing in yourself, but you had the confidence to come in here and talk to random strangers when you wanted to track down all your exes. That takes courage. Meeting with people you were intimate with after all these years, that takes guts too.'

'So you don't want to break up with me?' I asked, though having heard his speech I was pretty sure I was safe on that score after all.

'Break up with you? I don't ever want to be away from you,' he said.

I resolved then that even if his job took him to another city during the week, I'd find a way to make it work. We could take it in turns to travel at weekends. Jake was everything none of my previous boyfriends had been. He was the full package of kindness, humour, and gentle strength that I wanted. He was right for me, and I wasn't going to lose him just because of distance.

'So now what?' I asked him.

Chapter Thirty-Two

'Are you sure you want to do this?' Charmaine asked as I stood outside the door with a key. 'He did dump you so that he could go out with her.'

'I know,' I reminded her. 'I was there, but I've been thinking about what Steph told us at the hospital. I think Ryan knew that he wouldn't be able to control me forever. I had you and Matt and my parents, despite how much he tried to come between us. Tina had no one, not even me. He made sure of that and then he knew he could treat her however badly he wanted.' My hands were shaking, but I was determined to go through with it. 'They're going to release Ryan on bail tonight. Tina is being allowed out later too. If I don't get her stuff now, she'll have to risk seeing him again. No, I'm going to do this, I promised her I would. I'm not leaving her to cope on her own,' I said. I took a deep breath and opened the door.

'It was her decision to go out with him,' Charmaine pointed out as we walked in.

'You have no idea how manipulative he was,' I countered. 'Tina was so lonely back then. All it would have taken was a bit of flattery and some attention. I don't think she ever meant to hurt me.'

'If you say so,' my cousin muttered, looking around her.

Inside, the flat was pristine, much as it had been when I'd left it a year earlier. Ryan had always insisted that people took their shoes off when they walked in, so now I left mine on as I walked into the sitting room. The black leather sofa that Ryan had demanded be wiped clean once a week was still immaculate. The magazines were stacked neatly at right angles to the coffee table. Charmaine noticed this too and picked them up, turned half the wrong way round and left them fanned out all over the surface. It gave me a wonderful, terrible idea.

I grinned and walked over to the cupboard. Grabbing out a bag of Ryan's favourite Hobnobs, I stamped on the packet until it was no more than crumbs, then I opened it and poured it all over the sofa, taking the time to rub crumbs between the sofa cushions and under the armrests.

I walked into the bedroom and started to pack Tina's bags. I heard crashing from the kitchen. I figured Charmaine was having fun with Ryan's beer glass collection. I grinned and left her to it. I was too busy anyway. He'd always been upset that he couldn't grow a decent covering of facial hair so I helped by drawing moustaches all over photos of him. I'd always thought it was weird that a person kept framed photographs of themselves all over their bedroom.

It took barely half an hour to pack all of Tina's clothes and shoes. There were so few personal effects of hers in the flat. I guess this was another element of Ryan's controlling behaviour. We walked out and put the bags in the boot of my Mini. Looking at my watch, I realised that it still wasn't even lunchtime. I rang the police station and pretended to be Ryan's sister, asking what time I could pick him up. The officer explained that it would be about another two hours, and I found myself smiling.

'Do you think we could plan Ryan a special homecoming in the next two hours?' I asked Charmaine. She grinned, and we let ourselves back into the flat and got busy. Afterwards we collected Tina from the hospital and took her back to my flat to get settled in.

'Are you sure you don't mind me staying here for a bit?' she asked. 'I'll try and get myself sorted out soon. I've got another session with Steph tomorrow and she's going to help me.'

'There's no rush,' I assured her. 'Now, do you think Ryan knows where I live?'

Tina shook her head. 'I found out once. I drove past when you were letting yourself in, but I never told him.'

'That's good, but we can always see about getting a panic alarm fitted if you'd feel happier.'

'I've got my mobile. And your landline, if needs be. I think I feel okay here,' Tina assured me. 'Why, do you think he'll come looking for us?' she asked. 'I don't think he'll expect me to be with you. He thought he'd done a pretty good job of destroying our friendship.' I gave her hand a gentle squeeze.

'I'm glad he didn't,' I told her. 'But I don't think I want to see him anytime soon.'

'We need to go,' Charmaine reminded me. 'I promised Bea I'd teach her my sea bass recipe. She said that her ex used to do most of the cooking and she wants to learn a few new skills for herself. I've also got a chocolate torte that was left over from an event I catered yesterday for pudding.'

'You don't have to ask me twice,' I said. 'My mouth is watering at the thought of the cake. And I'm sure you have a veggie version of the sea bass all planned too?'

She ruffled my hair. 'Have I ever let you down, cousin?'

'Hey,' I said, shoving her hand away. 'But no, you never have,' I conceded.

'Bea has a pack of quorn fillets in her freezer. I'm sure I can jazz a few of those up for you somehow.'

'You're the best,' I told her.

'I know,' she said, with a grin.

Tina watched our banter without joining in, but as I grabbed my cardigan she gave a little cough. 'Do you think you might have enough for one more?' she asked.

Charmaine looked at me, waiting for me to agree before she said yes. I think she bore more of grudge than I did about Tina getting together with Ryan. I just felt guilty that I hadn't warned her and was happy to have my friend back.

Jake greeted me with a kiss that promised of more to come when we were alone. I held his hand while we walked through to the kitchen. Alice showed Tina her room, whilst Bea and Charmaine made quick work of cooking the tea.

Tina sat herself carefully at the table, wincing as she accidentally bumped her cheek when she took her sweater off. 'Do you need some painkillers?' Jake offered.

She shook her head. 'I want to feel this,' she told him. 'And remember that this is the last time I ever want to hurt this way.'

I wasn't sure I'd ever choose to be in pain if I didn't need to, but I could understand why she felt like that. Knowing that you would never go back was freeing.

'This is amazing,' Tina said as she tasted the fish. 'Ryan used to love sea bass.'

'I know,' Charmaine said. 'I found some that was a couple of days out of date when we went to the flat.'

'I'd been planning to cook it when we got back from the bar. He must have been in jail so long it went off,' Tina said, looking down at her lap. The fear of wasting food was one that had taken me a long time to recover from too.

'I wondered what was going round in the tumble dryer,' I said. Tina's mouth dropped open and I saw Jake smile as he looked at me. 'Was that you?' I asked. Charmaine nodded and took a sip of her wine. 'Don't worry,' I told Tina. 'I'm sure it'll be well cooked by the time Ryan gets home. I set it off on a three hour hot cycle for good measure.' Bea laughed and Tina continued to look at me.

'I might have accidentally tipped his aftershave out,' Charmaine added quietly. Bea reached over and gave her a high five. Tina looked like she was trying to overcome her fear for long enough to smile but was finding it tough. 'I thought he might like scented pillows. They might still be too soaked to use by tonight sadly. I guess he won't be tumble drying them though.'

'What else did you get up to?' Jake asked, his eyes sparkling with laughter.

'We only had two hours,' Charmaine pointed out.

'So we didn't do as much damage as we'd have liked,' I added.

'But if he tries to watch TV he'll have to retune every channel,' Charmaine said.

'When he finds where we hid all the cables, chargers and batteries,' I added. 'I unplugged his freezer too,' I continued. 'I'm hoping he won't spot that for a few days. He shouldn't go hungry tonight though, the twenty-four pizzas I ordered should be arriving at his flat any minute. Followed by a couple of taxis. All pre-paid on his credit card, the emergency one he still kept in his bedside drawer, to make sure that none of the businesses are left out of pocket, naturally.'

'I thought that was you on the phone,' Charmaine said. 'I picked it up and heard voices. It's okay though, once you finished I found an 0898 number at the back of the paper and dialled it. If he found that and hung up straight away when he got home it might only cost him about £120.'

Bea was grinning, and we weren't even halfway through our list yet.

'I noticed that the dishwasher hadn't been put on,' I said. 'I thought I'd do something useful after all my mischief and so I set it off for him. I might have accidentally used the wrong detergent though. What do you think happens if you put a whole bottle of fairy liquid in and switch it on?'

'He'll be mopping up for a week,' Jake said, leaning over and kissing me.

'I know it was juvenile, but I felt like I owed him,' I said.

'I have no problems with that at all,' Tina said, smiling. 'I half wish I was there to see his face when the floor floods. He once made me clean it with my toothbrush when I spilt my drink by accident.'

I found myself going quiet at the reminder that Ryan had been vicious, and that the punishments he had meted out had not been merely pranks.

'That makes me feel better about cutting holes in all his pants,' Charmaine said, and Tina giggled. Hiding it behind her hand, she laughed until her eyes watered.

'I might also have hidden his precious watches,' I added. Jake sat back and crossed his hands against his chest. 'Are you waiting for the punchline?' I asked. He nodded. 'I might have hidden them down the toilet.'

'We were running out of time by then, so we made a hit on the credit card Evie found and donated a thousand pounds to a women's refuge charity, then we came away.'

Tina got up and walked round the table. She hugged me, then threw her arms around Charmaine.

I wanted to stay with Jake that night, but I didn't think that Tina should be on her own. We still hadn't discussed his job interview, but I had no emotional energy spare to talk about it yet. He walked Tina and me back to my flat, kissed me and left. I was pretty sure that Ryan wouldn't be able to find her, but when her mobile rang at two a.m. and she shook as she answered it, I was glad to be there. I wasn't sure whether he would be full of apology for what he'd done and angling for Tina to drop the charges or if he'd be angry about his flat.

At first Tina seemed calm. She accepted his apologies and calmly but firmly told him that she wouldn't be dropping the charges against him. She assured Ryan that she had been in hospital and had no idea how his flat got trashed. She told him that it was nothing less than he deserved. By the time she hung up he was screaming down the phone at her, calling her all manner of names.

'I think we should phone the police tomorrow and let them know that he's still harassing you,' I said.

'What happens if he presses charges about the damage to the flat?' she asked. 'I don't want to get you and Charmaine into trouble.'

'We'll be fine.' I assured her. 'We wore gloves. Well, we needed to when we poured bleach all over his expensive suits. So no one saw us and there's no fingerprints. Besides, when the advert gets printed tomorrow he's going to be far too busy to worry about his flat any more.'

'I don't know if I'm so in awe of you or so nervous about this advert that I don't want to ask,' Tina said.

'It was Charmaine's idea.' I admitted. 'But it's a doozy. We saw the email address for classified ads in the paper when we were looking up premium rate numbers to call. Tomorrow the local paper has agreed to run a full-page special ad. You see, it turns out that Ryan has decided to publish an apology to any woman he has ever hurt, alongside his mobile number and photograph. He must have had a real change of heart; he wanted to admit to being a bully and a chauvinist. The newspaper rang on his landline within minutes of us sending it. You should have heard Charmaine talking in a gruff voice pretending to be him. I don't think they could believe it was real. The clincher though was that the stupid bastard was so arrogant, he was so sure you would never touch his stuff that he hadn't even bothered to put a password on his laptop. When they realised that the email came from his address, they agreed to run it.'

'I promise that I will never, ever, cross you again,' Tina said.

Chapter Thirty-Three

Tina settled herself in nicely at my flat and I pretty much moved in with Jake. I told myself that it was because I was making the most of my time with him before school started, but really I just wanted to hold him every chance I got, just in case he had to move soon for work. We spent mornings at the park, then Jake would take over for afternoons of drawing at home, or reading stories, or playing endless games of hide and seek, where he'd pretend not to be able to see Alice even when she hid in the same place for the fifth time or left her legs sticking out from under the bed sheets. I'd do paperwork, and we'd meet up again at the table for tea.

Each night I'd go to sleep next to Jake, counting down how many nights I had left of holiday. All too soon, it was Friday. The final day of official school holidays. Jake woke me up before Alice did. Bea had booked the day off so that she could take care of Alice and though I'd loved spending so much time with her this summer, I was looking forward to having Jake to myself for the day. Jake was excited too, as we were due at the hospital at ten to have his cast removed finally. He whispered some things in my ear that he was planning to do once he got the all clear. Some of his suggestions included him finally being able to join me in the bath or shower, and I enjoyed hearing his plans so much we ended up running out the door with only minutes to spare before his appointment.

I dropped him at the door and drove round to the car park. By the time I found a tiny space at the very top of the multi-storey block and made it back down to the fracture clinic, Jake had already had his cast removed by the technician and was waiting to see the doctor. Jake held his wrist carefully on his lap, trying not to touch it. I was fascinated, there was a fine scar down one side, and the skin was paler having missed out on six weeks of sunshine.

The doctor worked her way slowly through the waiting room. We saw the hyper kid who had been dancing round his exhausted mum go in and come out without a cast on his leg. An old lady with a broken arm went in and then left with her carer and a big smile. Another kid, a girl this time, with a broken foot hobbled in and out. She kept her cast but got given some amazing new crutches with purple handles that matched her trainers. She left with a grin too.

Finally the nurse called Jake in. By this time it was so hot in the waiting room we left sweaty outlines when we got up out of the plastic chairs. She pointed to a wooden chair in the side room and bustled around handing files to the doctor without saying another word to us.

'So you broke your wrist in a car accident six weeks ago,' the doctor said to Jake. Jake nodded. The doctor examined an X-ray plate and felt gently around his wrist. 'It seems to have healed well,' she said. 'I don't think you need the cast any more. Are you in any pain? No. Okay, you can go, just come back if you have any problems with it later.' She stood up, shook Jake's hand and showed us out of the room. We'd been in there less than five minutes.

'It's over,' Jake said, rolling his sleeves up outside and looking at his naked arm.

'What would you like to do now?' I asked as I inched my Mini out of the space. I was glad that I hadn't got a bigger car, even though Jake's knees were up around his chin. Maybe if we were spending lots of time driving to see each other soon I'd better think again. I found my good mood slipping away.

'Let's go home,' Jake said.

Thankfully Bea and Alice weren't back from their day out yet and we managed to work our way through a few of the things on Jake's wish list. We were dressed again and just mopping the last of the water up off the floor when the others got home. Bea looked at us and grinned. I'm glad Alice was too young to know what we'd been up to but I found myself blushing regardless.

Jake and I ducked into his room. He sat folding his clean clothes and putting them away. I sat on his bed, yawning even though it wasn't late yet. Our afternoon activities combined with the stress of the last few days had tired me out.

'Do you fancy a cuppa?' Jake asked, putting a T-shirt in his drawer and coming over to kiss me again.

'I'd love one, please,' I told him. I was about to ask for a couple of biscuits too, thinking that maybe the sugar might pick me up a bit, but my mobile rang. When Jake came back and handed me a mug I was still trying to get my head around what I'd just agreed to. 'That was my head teacher,' I told him. 'The guy who was supposed to be taking over as head of year eleven had a heart attack and is going to be off work for at least six months.'

'Oh no,' Jake responded, setting his own mug down next to mine.

'They were asking if I wanted to take it on instead,' I said. 'It's a bit daunting. Last year he had to support kids through three unplanned pregnancies, two arrests and one small international incident.'

'That sounds like a hell of a school,' Jake said with a wink.

'Normally I'd have run a mile,' I admitted. 'That level of responsibility at a school like mine is frankly, terrifying.'

'Did you turn them down?'

I shook my head. 'I must be crazy, but I didn't. If the last few weeks have left me with anything, it's the desire not to be scared any more. I said yes.'

Jake walked over and drew me in for a hug. 'I'm so proud of you,' he said, 'and I know you're going to be amazing. The kids are lucky to have you.'

'I guess we're both going to have a busy few weeks settling into new jobs,' I told him.

'About that,' he began, 'there's a bit of a hold up with my job.'

'What do you mean?' I asked. 'I'm so sorry, I've been so wrapped up in myself recently, I just assumed it was all going ahead.'

'It was,' he replied. 'At least, they offered it to me. I didn't want to turn them down flat, they're a great firm and when I applied it was in good faith that if they offered me the role that I'd take it. But my life has changed more in the last couple of months than I ever could have foreseen. When I spoke to you and I thought that it was you in hospital that night instead of Tina, I nearly lost the plot. I don't want to lose you, Evie.'

'You won't,' I assured him. 'I've been thinking about this non-stop too. And you won't lose me. I don't want to be without you either. But I don't want to stop you from taking an opportunity that would be good for you. I've been thinking about how we can take trains so that we can meet up, or maybe I can swap to a bigger car.'

'Evie, wait,' he said, taking my hands and sitting us both down on the bed. 'I rang the firm last week and talked it all through with them. They've agreed to hold on to my CV for now. They think that they should have some positions opening up in their London office within the next couple of months. I know Bea could do with the extra help until then. I was hoping you wouldn't mind having me around either.'

'Mind?' I asked, turning to face him and throwing my arms around his neck. I covered him with kisses and didn't stop until he pulled back to catch his breath.

'There's one more thing,' he said, getting up and walking over to his bedside drawer. 'I found this for you.' He pulled out a long black velvet box. 'I was at the train station on my way home, and all I could think of was getting back to you. They had a silver stall and I spotted this.' He opened the box and I saw a necklace with a pendant of two interconnected hearts. He picked it up and fastened the clasp around my neck. 'It isn't a ring,' he explained, 'because as I say, I haven't seen the most stunning examples of happy marriages, and with your experiences of being engaged I wasn't sure you would want that either yet, though I'm closer to thinking about marriage than I have ever been before.'

'I love it,' I said, tracing the pattern of the hearts with my fingertip.

'I was hoping you would accept it as a token of my commitment to you,' Jake said. 'Because this is how I feel. That your heart and mine are connected.'

'I feel the same way,' I told him.

Chapter Thirty-Four

The next few months were crazy busy. Life seemed determined to test how confident I was in my new role. I had meetings with social services, youth workers, and on one notable occasion we even had the police turn up. It was daunting, but I hid my nerves from both the students and the adults, and eventually I started to feel as confident as I was trying to act. When you've stood up to a uniformed officer and told them that they can't interrupt your lesson to interview a kid without their parent, and they've listened to you, you feel like you can take on anyone.

Of course, going home to Jake each night helped. The firm he had interviewed with was as good as their word. Within a few weeks he had a second interview and began working in an office just a few miles away. Sometimes he comes home from work buzzing because he loves what he is doing so much. You can't ask for more than that.

Tina had a few more angry calls from Ryan. He tried to pressure her into dropping the charges but she refused. When she turned up at a preliminary hearing at court, surrounded by me, Jake, Charmaine and Matt, he realised that he wasn't going to able to scare her off. Eventually he pleaded guilty so that he could get a reduced sentence. Three years didn't feel like enough for the hell he had put her through, but it gave her some breathing space at least.

Tina went back to work once her injuries had healed and decided to sublet my flat. She enjoyed the freedom of making her own rules, just as I had when I'd first left Ryan to live there. I worried that she would be nervous going out by herself, but she seemed to bounce back remarkably quickly. She had regular sessions with Steph to talk about what had happened. Matt seemed keen to help her too. I tried to nip round to check on her whenever I could, and he was there more and more often.

With Jake and I being able to contribute to the rent, Bea dropped down to working just two days a week, and she looked revitalised. I didn't complain about coming home after a long day at work to a hot dinner either, especially because she and Charmaine had a lot of fun practising their new meal ideas out on us.

Ted agreed to an organised plan of contact with Alice. Bea was nervous for the first overnight visit, but we distracted her by taking her for her first night out since Alice had been born. Even George and Zoe came to meet us at the pub. Zoe wasn't drinking. She announced that they'd made more than just a suntan on their honeymoon, and she and Bea spent the rest of the night talking pregnancy and babies. Charmaine pretended to look bored, but I think she was just making sure that I was okay about it, and I really was.

By now I only had a few pages left in my little black book. Jake offered to buy me a new one for Christmas, but I told him I didn't need it any more. I didn't need to spend hours writing about what had happened or trying to work out how I felt about it. For once it was crystal clear. I love him.

Thank You

Dear Reader,

Thank you for reading about Evie's Little Black Book. I hope that you enjoyed reading about how she got her confidence back as much as I enjoyed writing her journey. Writing this story has allowed me to have adventures when I wasn't really well enough to have any in real life. Thank you for joining me on them. I hope that no matter what and who is in your own Little Black Book, that you have as much love and happiness in your future and Evie and Jake do together.

I would like to thank the Ruby & Choc Lit family for welcoming me to the fold. Thanks too, to the Tasting panel for taking a chance on my books. I'm so excited to be on this adventure with such a welcoming and lovely group of people.

If you have enjoyed reading this story it would mean a lot to me if you had a few minutes to share a review. As a new writer, this is a great way for people to find out about my books.

If you have any thoughts, comments or questions you can contact me via twitter @HannahPearl_1

Hopefully I'll see you again when we share the next adventure together.

Hannah x

About the Author

Hannah Pearl was born in East London. She is married with two children and now lives in Cambridge.

She has previously worked as a Criminology researcher at a university in Leicester, as a Development Worker with various charities and even pulled a few pints in her time.

In 2015 she was struck down by Labrynthitis, which left her feeling dizzy and virtually housebound. She has since been diagnosed with ME. Reading has allowed Hannah to escape from the reality of feeling ill. She read upwards of three hundred books during the first year of her illness. When her burgeoning eReader addiction grew to be too expensive, she decided to have a go at writing. In 2017 she won Simon and Schuster's Books and the City #heatseeker short story competition, in partnership with *Heat* magazine, for her short story *The Last Good Day*.

Hannah is a member of the Romantic Novelists Association. *Evie's Little Black Book* is her debut novel.

Follow Hannah:
www.dizzygirlwrites.wordpress.com
Twitter: www.twitter.com/HannahPearl_1

More Ruby Fiction

From Hannah Pearl

It's My Birthday

Oh boy, another birthday …

Karen could be excused for crying on her birthday, especially as it's the first one since her husband got on a plane to the States and never came back. Then there's the fact that her workmates were practically bribed to attend her birthday meal. But when a restaurant double booking leads to her sharing a table with single dad Elliot and his daughter, things start looking up.

As Karen gets to know Elliot she experiences feelings she thought she'd never have again. But is it enough? Or will the thing that destroyed Karen's previous relationship also ruin things with Elliot?

Visit www.rubyfiction.com for details.

More from Ruby Fiction

Why not try something else from our selection:

The Best Boomerville Hotel

Caroline James

Let the shenanigans begin at the Best Boomerville Hotel ...

Jo Docherty and Hattie Contaldo have a vision – a holiday retreat in the heart of the Lake District exclusively for guests of 'a certain age' wishing to stimulate both mind and body with new creative experiences. One hotel refurbishment later and the Best Boomerville Hotel is open for business!

Perhaps not surprisingly Boomerville attracts more than its fair share of eccentric clientele: there's fun-loving Sir Henry Mulberry and his brother Hugo; Lucinda Brown, an impoverished artist with more ego than talent; Andy Mack, a charming Porsche-driving James Bond lookalike, as well as Kate Simmons, a woman who made her fortune from an internet dating agency but still hasn't found 'the One' herself.

With such an array of colourful individuals there's bound to be laughs aplenty, but could there be tears and heartbreak too and will the residents get more than they bargained for at Boomerville?

Visit www.rubyfiction.com for details.

The Purrfect Pet Sitter
Carol Thomas

Introducing Lisa Blake, the purrfect pet sitter!

When Lisa Blake's life in London falls apart, she returns to her hometown rebranding herself as 'the purrfect petsitter' – which may or may not be false advertising as she has a rather unfortunate habit of (temporarily) losing dogs!

But being back where she grew up, Lisa can't escape her past. There's her estranged best friend Flick who she bumps into in an embarrassing encounter in a local supermarket. And her first love, Nathan Baker, who, considering their history, is sure to be even more surprised by her drunken Facebook friend request than Lisa is.

As she becomes involved in the lives of her old friends Lisa must confront the hurt she has caused, discover the truth about her mysterious leather-clad admirer, and learn how to move forward when the things she wants most are affected by the decisions of her past.

Visit www.rubyfiction.com for details.

Introducing Ruby Fiction

Ruby Fiction is in imprint of Choc Lit Publishing.
We're an award-winning independent publisher,
creating a delicious selection of fiction.

See our selection here:
www.rubyfiction.com

Ruby Fiction brings you stories that inspire emotions.

We'd love to hear how you enjoyed *Evie's Little Black Book*.
Please visit www.rubyfiction.com and give your feedback
or leave a review where you purchased this novel.

Ruby novels are selected by genuine readers like yourself.
We only publish stories our Tasting Panel want to see in
print. Our reviews and awards speak for themselves.

Could you be a Star Selector and join our Tasting Panel?
Would you like to play a role in choosing which novels
we decide to publish? Do you enjoy reading women's
fiction? Then you could be perfect for our Tasting Panel.

Visit here for more details ...
www.choc-lit.com/join-the-choc-lit-tasting-panel

Keep in touch:
Sign up for our monthly newsletter Spread for all the latest
news and offers: www.spread.choc-lit.com. Follow us on
Twitter: @RubyFiction and Facebook: RubyFiction.

Stories that inspire emotions!